WJEC GCSE DESIGN & TECHNOLOGY

RESISTANT MATERIALS

MARTIN FRANKLIN

HODDER
EDUCATION
AN HACHETTE UK COMPANY

Orders: please contact Bookpoint Ltd, 130 Milton Park, Abingdon, Oxon OX14 4SB. Telephone: +44 (0)1235 8 27720. Fax: +44 (0)1235 400454. Lines are open from 9.00am to 5.00pm, Monday to Saturday, with a 24-hour message-answering service. You can also order through our website www.hoddereducation.co.uk

If you have any comments to make about this, or any of our other titles, please send them to educationenquiries@hodder.co.uk

British Library Cataloguing in Publication Data
A catalogue record for this title is available from the British Library

ISBN: 978 1 444 10858 3

First edition published 2010
Impression number   10 9 8 7 6 5 4 3 2 1
Year   2014 2013 2012 2011 2010

Hachette UK's policy is to use papers that are natural, renewable and recyclable products and made from wood grown in sustainable forests. The logging and manufacturing processes are expected to conform to the environmental regulations of the country of origin.

Cover photo © Maximillian Stock Ltd/2009 photolibrary.com
Illustrations by Oxford Designers & Illustrators
Typeset by Fakenham Photosetting Ltd, Fakenham, Norfolk
Printed in Italy for Hodder Education, an Hachette UK Company, 338 Euston Road, London NW1 3BH

CONTENTS

INTRODUCTION

Welcome to WJEC Design and Technology for GCSE Resistant Materials.

This book has been designed to support you throughout your GCSE course. It provides clear and precise guidance for successfully tackling the Controlled Assessment Task (CAT) and the examination.

The book:
- *is student focused. The aim of the book is to help you achieve the best possible results*
- *will be a help to you throughout the duration of your course*
- *gives you clear guidance of exactly what is expected of you in both the CAT and the examination*
- *contains examiner tips and guidance to help improve your performance in both the CAT and examination*
- *provides detailed information relating to the subject content and using the design process*
- *is designed to help you locate information quickly and easily*
- *is focused on the WJEC specification for GCSE Resistant Materials*
- *has relevance and value to other GCSE Resistant Materials courses.*

How to use this book

This book outlines the knowledge, skills and understanding required to successfully complete the GCSE Resistant Materials Technology course. It is designed to provide you with the knowledge and guidance necessary to complete the Controlled Assessment Task and the examination and will enhance the knowledge and understanding you will be developing in your lessons and class work.

The design process

Design and technology is about designing and making. Chapter 1 provides you with guidance to tackle design-and-make activities and takes you through the fundamental aspects of the design process. This will help you in your class work, when tackling the CAT and when answering the general design question in the examination.

Unit 1: The examination paper

Chapters 2–8 give detailed and specific knowledge and information required to tackle the examination. Chapter 9 then provides you with particular guidance and advice on the format of the examination and how to tackle different types of questions.

Unit 2: Controlled Assessment Task (CAT)

Chapter 1 provides you with information and guidance related to the designing section of the CAT.

Chapters 2–8 will give you the technical knowledge and information you will require, while Chapter 10 will give you specific details and guidance about each of the pages of the CAT.

You will be able to refer to this book prior to starting the CAT and when you are working under timed conditions during the CAT itself.

Icons used in this book

Introduction boxes provide a short overview of the topics under discussion in the section.

KEY POINTS

• Key Points boxes list key aspects of a topic.

KEY TERM

Key Terms boxes provide definitions of the technical terms used in the section.

EXAMINER'S TIPS

Examiner's Tips boxes give tips on how to improve performance in both the Controlled Assessment and examined units.

ACTIVITY

Activity boxes suggest interesting tasks to support, enhance and extend learning opportunities.

LEARNING OUTCOMES

Learning Outcomes boxes highlight the knowledge and understanding you should have developed by the end of the section.

 ## QUESTIONS

Questions boxes provide practice questions to test key areas of the content of the specification.

ACKNOWLEDGMENTS

The author and publishers would like to thank the following for permission to use copyright material in this book:

Figure 1.9 © Design Pics Inc./Alamy; Figure 1.10 © Digital Vision; Figure 1.11 George Doyle/Stockdisc/Getty Images; Figure 1.12 © Purestock; Figure 1.13 OCR D&T Resistant Materials Technology exam paper 1956/4 (14 June 2006) reproduced with permission from OCR; Figure 1.18 OCR D&T: Resistant Materials Technology exam paper 1956/4 (16 June 2005) reproduced with permission from OCR; Figure 1.19 OCR D&T: Resistant Materials Technology exam paper 1956/4 (13 June 2007) reproduced with permission from OCR; Figure 1.28 OCR D&T: Resistant Materials Technology exam paper 1462/4 (14 June 2001) reproduced with permission from OCR; Figure 1.32 TechSoft UK Ltd; Figure 1.36 OCR D&T Resistant Materials Technology exam paper 1462/3 (14 June 2001) reproduced with permission from OCR; Figure 1.37 OCR D&T Resistant Materials Technology exam paper 1956/4 (16 June 2004) reproduced with permission from OCR; Figure 1.41 OCR D&T Resistant Materials Technology exam paper 1956/2 (26 May 2005) reproduced with permission from OCR; Figure 1.45 OCR D&T Resistant Materials Technology exam paper 1462/3 (9 June 1998) reproduced with permission from OCR; Figure 2.1 © igor terekhov/iStockphoto.com; Figure 2.2 © Elena Schweitzer/iStockphoto.com; Figure 2.3 © Lovegrove Studio; Figure 2.4a © Yury Shirokov – Fotolia.com; Figure 2.4b © adisa – Fotolia.com; Figure 2.5 © David Asch – Fotolia.com; Figure 2.6 © photogl – Fotolia.com; Figure 2.7a © picturefrank – Fotolia.com; Figure 2.7b © Diana Mastepanova – Fotolia.com; Figure 2.8 © igor terekhov/iStockphoto.com; Figure 3.2 © Andrey Prokhorov/iStockphoto.com; Figure 3.3 © Tye Carnelli/iStockphoto.com; Figure 3.4 © Achim Prill/iStockphoto.com; Figure 3.5 © Marcus Clackson/iStockphoto.com; Figure 3.6 © Olivier Blondeau/iStockphoto.com; Figure 3.7 © Gary Unwin – Fotolia.com; Figure 3.8 © Dawn Hudson – Fotolia.com; Figure 3.9 Reproduced with permission; Figure 3.10 © Dena Steiner/iStockphoto.com; Figure 3.12 reprinted with kind permission by EU Ecolabel; Figure 3.13 © Jaap Hart/iStockphoto.com; Figure 3.15 © BAO-RF – Fotolia.com; Figure 3.17b © Dieter K. Henke/iStockphoto.com; Figure 3.18 © Dallas Powell – Fotolia.com Figure 4.1 © J.+W Roth – Fotolia.com; Figure 4.2 Philippe Psaila/Science Photo Library; Figure 4.4 Rosenfeld Images Ltd/Science Photo Library; Figure 4.5 Boxford Ltd; Figure 4.7 © Dan Barnes/iStockphoto.com; Figure 5.2 © The Carlin Company/iStockphoto.com; Figure 5.14 © Maurice van der Velden/iStockphoto.com; Figure 5.16a © anzeletti/iStockphoto.com; Figure 5.16b © Chris Elwell/iStockphoto.com; Figure 5.25b RTimages/iStockphoto.com; Figure 5.25a © Ahmad Faizal/iStockphoto.com; Figure 7.4 © Oksana Perkins/iStockphoto.com; Figure 7.18 C R Clarke & Co Ltd; Figure 7.24 C R Clarke & Co Ltd; Figure 7.41 Photodisc/Getty Images; Figure 7.42 © Tom Fewster/iStockphoto.com; Figure 7.43 © vnlit – Fotolia.com; Figure 7.44 © xyno/iStockphoto.com; Figure 7.45 © Ules Barnwell/iStockphoto.com; Figure 8.1 Techsoft UK Ltd; Figure 8.2a Techsoft UK Ltd; Figure 8.2b Techsoft UK Ltd; Figure 8.3 Techsoft UK Ltd; Figure 8.4 Techsoft UK Ltd;

Figure 8.5 Techsoft UK Ltd; Figure 8.11 Techsoft UK Ltd; Figure 8.12 © Golkin Oleg/iStockphoto.com; Figure 8.14 Courtesy of DS SolidWorks Corp.; Figure 8.15 Courtesy of DS SolidWorks Corp.; Figure 8.16 © Onur Döngel/iStockphoto.com; Figure 8.17 Techsoft UK Ltd; Figure 8.18 © Ivonne Wierink – Fotolia.com; Figure 8.19 Techsoft UK Ltd; Figure 8.20 Techsoft UK Ltd; Figure 8.21 Boxford Ltd; Figure 8.22 Boxford Ltd; Figure 8.24 © Chris Fertnig/iStockphoto.com; Figures 10.06–10.19 CAT worksheets reproduced with permission from WJEC.

Microsoft product screenshots reprinted with permission from Microsoft Corporation.

Every effort has been made to trace and acknowledge ownership of copyright. The publishers will be glad to make suitable arrangements with any copyright holders whom it has not been possible to contact.

DEVELOPING, PLANNING AND COMMUNICATING IDEAS

By the end of this chapter you should have developed a knowledge and understanding of:

- contexts and user groups
- the design brief and how to analyse it by asking and answering a number of key questions
- the need for technological knowledge as a prerequisite of good design
- why the most successful design proposal is often a compromise between conflicting requirements of size, form, materials, methods of construction and finish
- methods of gathering and analysing information and drawing conclusions from information
- what a design specification is and how to write a design specification for a product
- generating and effectively communicating a range of potential solutions to a problem
- evaluating a range of design ideas, identifying the strengths and weaknesses of each, and choosing the most promising for further development
- the information required on a working drawing.
- the importance of fully developing your best design ideas and the range of ways you can develop your ideas
- the importance of modelling and techniques used for 2D and 3D modelling
- how 2D modelling software, digital cameras and digital sound and video can be used in designing and making a model
- how to make a stage-by-stage plan for making a product
- the importance of quality assurance and quality control

- the requirements that need to be considered when choosing the most suitable material for a component or product.
- testing your product and the importance of other people's views
- recording the changes you have made from your working drawing and making further product development.

This chapter looks at the process of designing, which starts with an initial problem and concludes with a proposed solution. It also looks at the various issues that can and should influence the outcome of the final design.

1.1 IDENTIFICATION OF A DESIGN NEED

The first stage in designing a new product is identifying a real problem that needs to be solved. It is also important to consider who the users of the product will be.

The problems that you are likely to be involved in solving in your GCSE Design and Technology course will usually arise from everyday situations. Describing the situation where there is a need for a product is called the context.

Context

The context is why there is a need for a new product; for example:

(a) You have a large selection of CDs in your bedroom. They are untidy and it is difficult to find the one you want to listen to.

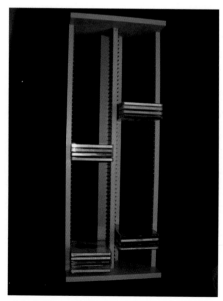

Figure 1.1 CDs left around a bedroom

Figure 1.2 A CD storage system

(b) You keep getting your keys mixed up with the keys that belong to other members of your family and you need some way to tell which keys are yours.

Figure 1.3 Four sets of keys

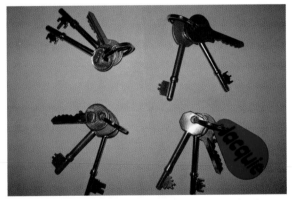

Figure 1.4 One set of keys is clearly identified

(c) You have a collection of pens and pencils that you take to school, but they keep getting lost in your bag and sometimes they get damaged. You need something to keep them all together and protect them when you are travelling to school and from lesson to lesson.

Figure 1.5 A collection of pens and pencils

Figure 1.6 A container for pens and pencils

(d) When you are sitting on an easy chair, having a cup of coffee, you put your mug on the floor, but it keeps getting knocked over accidentally and it is awkward to

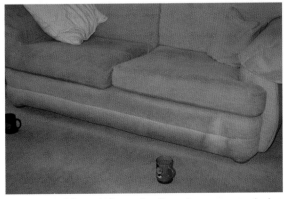

Figure 1.7 Mugs left on the floor by an easy chair

keep reaching down every time you want to have a drink.

Figure 1.8 A small oak coffee table

▶ User group

A user group is a description of a group of people who are likely to use the product you are designing. Examples of user groups are:

(a) Teenage boys and girls.

Figure 1.9 A group of teenage boys and girls

(b) Young men leaving home to go to university.

Figure 1.10 A group of 18-year-old men

(c) newly married couple.

Figure 1.11 A newly married couple

(d) Children between the ages of eight and ten.

Figure 1.12 A group of eight- to ten-year-old boys and girls

As you can see from the above examples, it is important that the user group you identify is not too wide. People's needs and preferences about a product will change dramatically from one user group to another. You should also think about the gender of your intended user group. Is it to be designed for male users, female users or both?

▶ The design brief

This is a short statement relating to the context and user group you have identified. It is important that the design brief is worded in such a way that you do not make assumptions about what the product will look like or any other details about the product you might eventually make. So a good design brief would be to 'design and make a product to keep a two-year-old child amused on a long journey'. A poor example of a similar brief would be 'design and make a red toy lorry'.

KEY TERMS

CONTEXT – The situation that has given rise to a product being needed.
USER GROUP – A clearly defined group of people who will be the users of a product.
DESIGN BRIEF – A carefully written, short statement giving the context and user group for a new product.

QUESTION

This question is based on the theme of mechanical reachers. Figure 1.13 shows a hand-held mechanical reacher.

Identify two different user groups who might use a hand-held reacher.

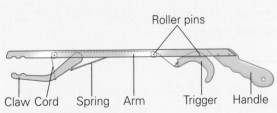

Roller pins

Claw   Cord   Spring   Arm   Trigger   Handle

Figure 1.13 Mechanical reacher

ACTIVITY

Manufacturers produce children's toys in large quantities. The designer uses a design brief to meet the requirements of the need, the user and the potential market.

In the table below, tick one statement that would be the most suitable design brief for a toy manufacturer.

Design brief	
Design a brightly coloured and safe toy for my own use	
Design an educational toy suitable for children between the ages of three and five years that could be batch-produced	
Design a red lorry with wheels, suitable for boys	
Design and make a toy suitable for young children	

Table 1.1

1.2 ANALYSING A DESIGN BRIEF

The short statement given in the design brief does not give sufficient information about the problem we are aiming to resolve by designing a new product. Therefore a full investigation into the problem is needed. This investigation is known as analysing the design brief.

One way of analysing a design brief is to use the five Ws method.

(1) **W**ho will use the product?

This may be a particular individual or groups of people and should have been clearly defined in the user group part of the first section. It is important to think carefully about what the people in your user group prefer and what they need from the product.

(2) **W**here will the product be used?

You need to think carefully about where exactly your product will be used. For example:

- a particular room of the house such as a kitchen or lounge
- a vehicle
- a garden
- a public place such as a park or beach.

Sometimes a product may be for a very specific place, such as for use on a table by the side of a bed or on a desk in an office.

(3) **W**hy is the product needed?

You need to state clearly the problem the product is required to solve. This will involve thinking carefully about the context of the design problem, as detailed earlier in this chapter.

(4) **W**hat precisely does the product have to do?

You need to consider carefully exactly what the product has to do. For example, a storage system for DVDs may need to:

- store 50 DVDs
- store DVDs so that the titles can be read easily
- enable each DVD to be placed into the storage system and removed easily
- enable the collection of 50 DVDs to be moved easily from room to room.

(5) **W**hen will the product be used?

Some products may be used at particular times or when certain activities are taking place, as in the examples below:

- A lamp may be used for background lighting when a family is watching TV or listening to music.
- A case for a guitar may be used when the musician is travelling to a performance or a rehearsal session.
- A chopping board will be used when salad, vegetables or fruit are being prepared for a meal.
- A parasol may be used when the sun becomes too strong to sit comfortably in the sun on a summer's day.

KEY TERM

THE FIVE Ws – Where and when the product will be used, who will use it, why it will be used and what it will be used for.

1.3 LINKING PRINCIPLES OF GOOD DESIGN AND TECHNOLOGICAL KNOWLEDGE

Producing a design is far from just producing a drawing of a product. Once an idea has been produced it needs to be developed into a final design proposal. This process is all about making decisions about size, form, method of construction, materials and finish.

Developing an initial idea for a product into a final product proposal is a very complex process. The designer needs to have good technological knowledge of materials, methods of construction and finish. When making a decision about each of these aspects of a design, the designer needs to be aware of the range of possibilities that he or she can choose from, and the advantages and disadvantages each of these possibilities will bring to the product.

Making a decision about one of these aspects is difficult in itself. For example, to make a decision about the material to be used for a component, the designer may need to consider:

- functional requirements
- economic considerations
- availability
- manufacturing method
- visual properties of the material
- the size and form of the product.

A similar range of considerations can be drawn up for the size and form of the component, the method of construction and the finish. Therefore, making a decision about each of these aspects of a design is a complex process.

Unfortunately, developing a final design proposal is not just about choosing the most promising size and form, material, method of construction and finish for a component in isolation. Some combinations are impossible or undesirable. It would not be possible to manufacture a component from vacuum-formed plywood, for example, as only thermoplastics can be vacuum-formed. All of these decisions need to be considered together. The best design will be the combination of size and form, material, method of construction and finish that offers the best *compromise* between all these aspects of the design.

Figure 1.14 A piece of vacuum-formed thermoplastic

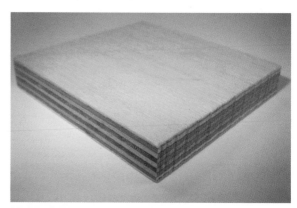

Figure 1.15 A piece of plywood

1.4 GATHERING RESEARCH AND INFORMATION

Once you have analysed your design brief, you can start researching your project. In this stage of your project you will gather information about what the people in your user group would like and prefer. You will look carefully at products that are already on the market and that do a similar job to the product you are designing.

EXAMINER'S TIPS

You will not need to present and submit your research when carrying out your Controlled Assessment Task (CAT), but it is important you thoroughly investigate your problem and take this into the CAT with you, as it will help you when you are analysing and designing your product.

What do the people in your user group want?

The first piece of research you will need to undertake is to find out exactly what the people in your user group want. This will include:

- establishing exactly what they want the product to do

- any particular features they would like the product to have

- any preferences they may have about the appearance of the product

- information about what the user group would find acceptable in terms of the life expectancy, maintenance and environmental aspects of the product

- how much your user group would be prepared to pay for the product you are designing

- information about ergonomic considerations that will influence the design of the product.

How to find out what people want

One of the most popular ways of finding out what people want is to design a questionnaire and hand it out for people to complete. It is important only to give out your questionnaire to people who are in the user group you have identified for your product, as asking the wrong people could give you very misleading results.

Conducting an in-depth interview with a small number of people can also give you valuable information about what your user group would like to see in your product. If you are going to conduct interviews you will need to think carefully about the questions you are

going to ask and make careful notes about the answers people give.

Looking at existing products

Looking at products that do a similar job to the product you are designing is a very useful source of information and ideas. Look carefully at the similar products you have identified and start by recording factual information about them. This will include:

- cost

- size

- weight

- the materials that have been used

- the methods of construction that have been used

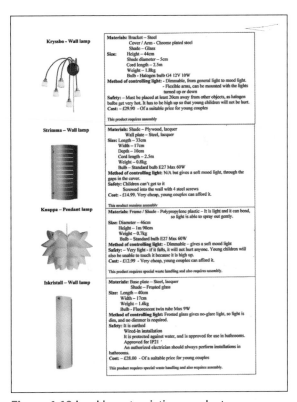

Figure 1.16 Looking at existing products

- the finish that has been applied to the product
- features the product has that enable it to do the job for which it was designed
- features that are common to some of the existing products you are looking at
- safety features.

Finding important factual information

It is likely that you will need to find out some essential factual information, particularly when you start to design your product in detail. For example, if you are designing a storage system you must know the size of all the objects you are going to store. It will also be necessary to find factual information about where the product is going to be used. The physical size of the people who are going to use the product will be important too. Anthropometric data will give average sizes of people in your user group that you can use when designing your product.

KEY TERMS

EXISTING PRODUCTS – Products which are already being manufactured and sold that do a similar job to the product you are designing.

ANTHROPOMETRIC DATA – Tables of the average measurements of people of a certain age and sex.

1.5 DEVELOPING A DESIGN SPECIFICATION

A design specification is a list of requirements that a product must meet. The design specification is written as a result of all the information you have gathered during your research.

Writing a design specification

A design specification should be written as a list of concise but detailed statements in bullet form. Each statement should be *specific* to the problem you are solving, so 'it must weigh less than 400 g' is far better than 'it must be light'.

It is a good idea to then justify why each point is important; for example, 'it must weigh less than 400 g so that the product can be easily carried by the child'.

The design specification will be used as a checklist when deciding which of your design ideas you are going to develop. It will also help you develop your design into a final solution and will be the basis of your evaluation when you will consider how your final product meets your specification.

The importance of each specification point can be organised under headings such as 'Essential criteria' and 'Desirable criteria'.

Another way is by writing lists of sentences starting with 'It must . . .' for the most important requirements, 'It should . . .' for less important considerations, and finally 'It could . . .' for features that would be an added bonus.

You may decide to put your specification into a table like this to organise your work:

Specification point	Why is it important in my project?	Level of importance	How will I evaluate its success?

Table 1.2

The headings listed below are a useful guide when writing a design specification. Not all of these headings will apply to all products.

Use and performance

This section will list the main purpose of the product, its essential features and any other particular requirements of the product. For example, the specification for a CD rack may include the following:

- It must store at least 50 CDs.
- It must store CDs so that the title of each CD is readable.
- It must allow each CD to be stored and removed from the rack easily.

Safety

Safety is one area that cannot be compromised. It is essential that your product complies with all relevant safety standards. In this section it is important that you try to think of all the safety problems that are particularly relevant to your product, such as electrical safety, trapping fingers, sharp edges and so on.

Size

It is likely that you will need to state the maximum or minimum size for a product, and in some cases you may need to state both a maximum and a minimum. Remember, it is much better to say, 'It must be no higher than 300 mm', than, 'It must be as short as possible'.

Weight

The maximum or minimum weight is often important when designing a product. For example, if you are designing a toy for a young child, it would be important that the product is light enough for the child to pick up easily with one hand. A sign to display information in a car park, on the other hand, may have to be fairly heavy so that it does not blow over in the wind.

Appearance

When writing a specification it is important to consider all aspects of appearance, such as shape, colours and textures.

Cost

No matter how good a product is, there is a maximum price that a consumer will pay for it. In most cases it will be sufficient to state the maximum cost of materials. For example, 'It must not cost more than £5.00 for the raw and pre-manufactured materials.'

Expected life

All products will eventually wear out and stop working. How long a product has to last in good working order will have a great influence on the quality of materials, components and manufacturing methods that will need to be used.

Maintenance

Most products will need some form of maintenance from time to time. Products that require less maintenance will be more expensive to make. It may be necessary, therefore, to state in your specification what level of maintenance would be acceptable for the product you are designing.

Environmental requirements

Environmental issues are very important and it may be necessary to state the maximum amounts of certain materials to be used. It may also be necessary to avoid some materials altogether or provide information about how a product can be recycled at the

end of its useful life. The manufacturing processes used to produce a product will also be important in relation to what impact a product will have on the environment.

Ergonomics

Ergonomics is about how products interact with people. This interaction takes place through the five senses – sight, sound, smell, taste and touch. You will need to consider each of these and write down any requirements that will be important for the product you are considering.

KEY TERM

ERGONOMICS – The way in which a product interacts with people through the five senses.

Figure 1.17 A specification for a jewellery container

ACTIVITY

Figure 1.18 shows two different industrially manufactured bedside lights. The lampshades and fittings have been removed.

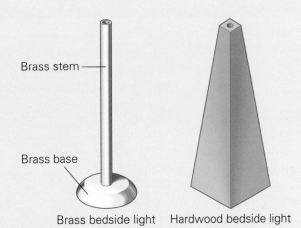

Brass stem

Brass base

Brass bedside light   Hardwood bedside light

Figure 1.18

1. A bedside light must:
   - be electrically safe
   - have a surface finish that would protect it.

   Add **two** more points to the specification.

2. Figure 1.19 shows an incomplete design for a key box to be used in a factory. The box is made from steel and wall-mounted using the three fixing holes.

Complete the following **two** specification points for the key box and provide a third specification point of your own.

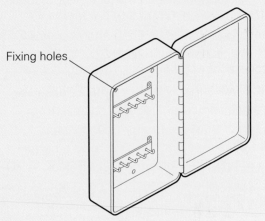

Fixing holes

Figure 1.19

The key box must:

(a) be made from a strong material because _____.

(b) allow easy access for the keys because _____.

(c) _____ because _____.

1.6 GENERATING AND COMMUNICATING DESIGN IDEAS

After a specification has been written, you can begin to create ideas for a product to meet the specification you have created for it. These ideas will be recorded and communicated initially by making sketches for as many ideas as you can. Your designs should demonstrate a variety and range of ideas, as you will gain marks for being creative and innovative.

Sketching

Sketching is a good way of recording ideas quickly. Keep drawing simple initial concepts until you have a wide range of possible approaches to consider. Make sure your ideas are completely different and not just variations on one idea. Freehand sketches can be drawn in either 2D or 3D. A 2D sketch is a good method of showing the details of an idea. It will show what the product looks like from one particular direction, such as from the top or from the front. A 3D sketch is more difficult to draw, but will give a better idea of how the whole product will look. A 3D sketch will show the top, front and one end of the product.

Always start a sketch with a cuboid just big enough to contain the shape you want to draw and then draw the shape inside the cuboid. This method is called 'crating' and will help you to produce quality 3D sketches of your ideas.

Shading

Pictorial views are used to give an overall view of an object, but these views will still only be 2D line drawings of a 3D object. Shading is needed to give the object the appearance of being solid. There are a number of ways of achieving this using a wide range of media.

When shading an object it is very important to consider which direction the light is coming from, so that you can work out which surfaces have light falling directly on them and which surfaces will appear darker because they are in shadow. Figure 1.21 shows a rectangular block with light falling on it from the direction shown. The block has been shaded to show a solid appearance.

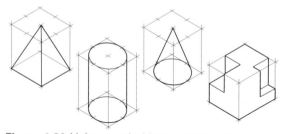

Figure 1.20 Using a cuboid to contain a shape

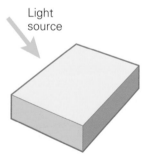

Figure 1.21 A shaded rectangular block

Pencil crayons can be used to produce some excellent results if used with care. The pencil needs to be used at a very low angle so that the side of the lead is used and not the point. Do not put any pressure on the pencil; just use the weight of the pencil itself and keep the shading very light. Just use the slightest hint of colour on the lightest surfaces, with slightly more on surfaces that are in shade.

Figure 1.24 Wood grain added with a darker pencil

Figure 1.22 Shading using the side of the pencil

Marker pens can also be used to shade an area. You need to use a pen with a wide chisel point and try not to overlap each stroke of the pen, as overlapped areas will appear darker. It is very difficult to keep sharp edges with a marker pen, so just go over the whole area, then cut out the shape and remount it on a second piece of paper. Marker pens are very useful for representing products made from opaque plastic.

Metals are very shiny, so to represent metal you need to show the highlights. This is best done by leaving areas with no colour at all or by using a white pencil to draw in highlights over the base colour.

Figure 1.25 Metal is represented by showing the highlights

Adding notes to your sketches

You can draw attention to part of your idea or explain a particular feature by adding notes to your sketches. Make sure you place these around your drawings and not on the drawing itself. Make sure your notes are concise and clearly written.

Figure 1.23 Shading using a marker pen

Textures

Adding a texture to a shaded sketch is very useful to indicate the material a product is made from. Wood grain can be added using a darker pencil.

KEY TERMS

SKETCH – A quickly produced drawing showing some details of a product.
SHADING – Adding colour to a drawing to make it look more solid and three-dimensional.

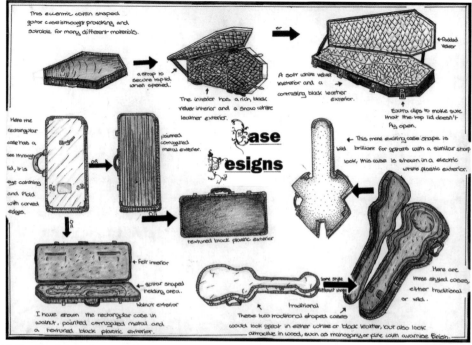

Figure 1.26 Design ideas for a guitar case

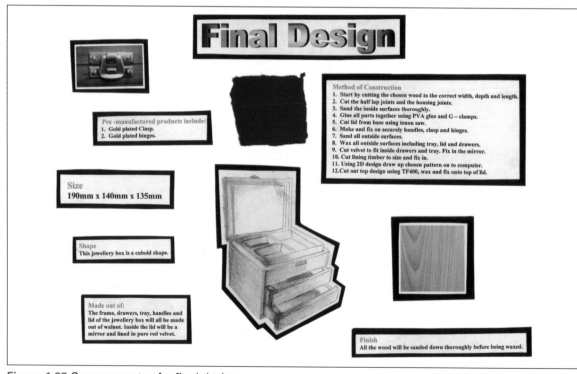

Figure 1.27 Some aspects of a final design

ACTIVITY

A school uses a range of hand tools for design and technology activities. Included in this range is a hot-glue gun, as shown in Figure 1.28.

Using notes and sketches, design a portable hot-glue gun holder. Your design must show:

Figure 1.28 A hot-glue gun

(a) stability of storage for the hot-glue gun on a bench worktop
(b) safe protection of children from the hot nozzle
(c) a means of containing any nozzle leaks of hot-melt glue.

1.7 DEVELOPING IDEAS

It is very important to fully develop your best design idea in order to produce a successful final product. In the CAT you will be expected to produce five pages of development, each focusing on a different aspect of your idea.

The development section will take the initial idea and turn it into a design that can be manufactured in resistant materials. You will need to consider aspects such as the size/dimensions, construction and the materials to be used. It is usually easier and clearer to develop these different aspects of your design separately. Remember the development is not necessarily a 2D exercise; try and include a range of modelling and trialling techniques.

Style and function of the chosen idea

For your chosen idea you will need to consider the function of your design – what the design must do and its aesthetics as well as what it looks like and how it could be improved. Use notes to justify your changes in this section. At the end of this section the developed solution may bear little resemblance to the initial idea or it may be very similar. Models can be made and photographs pasted onto the sheet, and computer-aided design (CAD) may be used if considered appropriate.

The range of materials and components that could be used

You should consider a range of possible materials for your chosen design and make reasoned decisions based on a variety of criteria:

- aesthetics – colour, decoration, pattern, etc.
- function – durability, weight, strength, conductivity, ease of use, etc.
- cost
- availability
- safety.

Try to relate this section directly to the product and do not simply produce a table of materials.

Exploring ways of making/constructing the idea

Try to consider different ways of constructing your product. This may include:

- different joints
- permanent and temporary fixings
- different processes
- use of CAD/computer-aided manufacture (CAM)
- joining like and unlike materials.

Developing the size and/or quantity of the design

This will be dependent on a range of factors, including:

- the dimensions of the parts, components or products the design must hold
- the number of parts, components or products the design must hold
- where the design will go
- how it can be used efficiently
- multiple numbers of identical parts.

You will probably need to refer back to your preliminary research regarding dimensions of

parts, components or products. Try to justify and annotate your reasoning. Some reference to maximum sizes, cutting or working areas of machinery, equipment or materials may be necessary.

Achieving a quality finish

The finish and the quality-control issues necessary to achieve it are important in order to ensure a good-quality final product. You will need to consider aspects such as:

- a range of possible finishes
- the processes/stages necessary to achieve a quality finish
- the advantages and disadvantages of each finish
- accuracy and consistency
- time allocation
- skill levels required
- the relevant quality-control issues to achieve a good finish.

Working drawings

You will need to show all the information that is needed to enable your product to be made. It is not important how this information is recorded and communicated, but it will require a combination of drawings and notes. You will need to show full details of:

- the shape of each component to be made
- the size of each component to be made
- details of the method of construction to be used
- the materials to be used for each component
- details of the finish to be used on each component

- details of any pre-manufactured components
- how all the components fit together.

This is a good opportunity to use CAD if appropriate. Try to consider whether you have provided sufficient information for the product to be made by a third party.

1.8 DEVELOPING USING MODELLING AND TRIALLING TECHNIQUES

Making a model of a design idea is an excellent way of developing an idea into a final design proposal that can be made in resistant materials. A model will allow you to explore the problems you may encounter in making the final product. It is also an excellent way of showing how the final product will look.

Models can be either 2D or 3D. A 2D model is excellent for exploring some details, such as how a mechanism will work. A 3D model is excellent for working out practical details, such as how different parts of the product will be fastened together. Models are normally made using materials that are easy to cut, shape and join. Popular materials for modelling are card, balsa wood and foam. Models can be made to scale or made to the same size as the final product.

Models are very useful as they can be made more quickly and cheaply than making a product in resistant materials.

Paper and card models

Paper and card are commonly used materials because they are available in a range of colours and thicknesses. They are also cheap

and easy to cut. They can be joined easily using glue or double-sided tape.

Figure 1.29 Ideas for lamps modelled from card

Foam models

Cutting and shaping high-density polystyrene foam is a fast way of creating solid models to make sure that you get the size and shape of your final product right. The foam is supplied in rectangular blocks which can be cut easily using hand tools and some power tools. The best way of approaching this kind of modelling is to build up the shape you need from smaller individual blocks that can be glued together, rather than cutting the shape from a very large single block.

Each piece is first drawn on the block of foam and then cut out using a vibrasaw or bandsaw. Final shaping and finishing can then be carried out using a file and abrasive paper.

To colour the model, use acrylic or emulsion paints. When this is dry, further painted detail can be added.

KEY TERM

PRODUCT MODELLING – A representation of a product, produced to enable a product to be visualised or further developed, or to solve particular design problems.

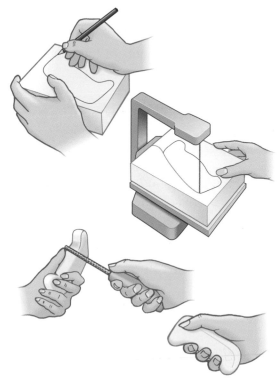

Figure 1.30 Marking out a block of foam

1.9 DIGITAL MEDIA AND NEW TECHNOLOGIES

Digital media and new technologies have developed enormously over the last few years, and designers at all levels have been very quick to use these methods for both designing and making.

Three-dimensional modelling software

Computer software such as Pro/DESKTOP and SolidWorks® is now widely available. These systems allow 3D photorealistic models to be produced. These models can be used to develop design ideas and are a valuable aid to visualising what a product will look like when it is made. This software is

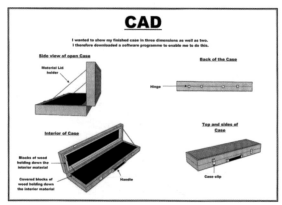

Figure 1.31 A product modelled using 3D modelling software

excellent for checking the proportion of a product or trying out different colour schemes.

Digital cameras

Digital cameras do not use film, so other than the camera itself there is no cost involved in taking a picture with a digital camera. The images captured can be fed directly into a computer, which is ideal if you are presenting your design folder in an electronic format. If you are presenting your design folder on paper, you will need to print your pictures and mount them onto your design sheets. Digital cameras are ideal for recording research and the development stages of your design work.

Rapid prototyping

Several systems are now available that enable components to be made directly from designs drawn on a computer. These machines do not cut the component from solid blocks or sheets of material, but build up the shape by solidifying powder or liquids. Computer software is used to slice up the 3D design into a series of layers which are then sent, in order, to the rapid prototyping machine, which builds up the solid component layer by layer.

Laser cutters

Laser cutters are an excellent way of cutting sheet, card, timber and plastic. They work by vaporising the material along a very narrow line. They do not work on metals because the laser is reflected by the surface of the metal. These machines are very good for making very professional models quickly. Nets made from card can be easily made as the cutter will both score and cut. To use a laser cutter, the design is first drawn using CAD. Speed and power settings need to be made on the computer software and the design is then sent to be cut. It is a very easy system to use, particularly as no work holding is needed.

Figure 1.33 A card model and a product cut from acrylic using a laser cutter

Figure 1.32 A rapid prototyping machine

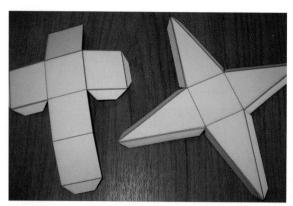

Figure 1.34 Nets cut from card with a laser cutter

Laser cutters will also engrave wood, plastic and coated metals, which creates further opportunities to enhance products very easily and to a very high standard.

Figure 1.35 Examples of engraving using a laser cutter

KEY TERMS

CAD – Producing a design by drawing on a computer using a software package (computer-aided design).

CAM – Cutting a component for a product by using a machine controlled by a computer (computer-aided manufacturing).

THREE-DIMENSIONAL MODELLING – Producing 3D photorealistic models using computer software.

QUESTIONS

1. Figure 1.36 shows a card model of an adjustable lamp.

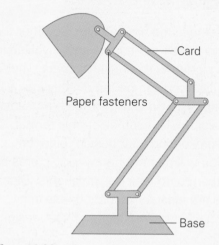

Card

Paper fasteners

Base

Figure 1.36

   (a) Give two reasons why making such a model could help in developing the design of the lamp.

   (b) State a design factor that this card model cannot tell us about the manufactured lamp when it is in use.

2. Designers use different types of modelling in the design process. Figure 1.37 shows two different models for the design of a wooden bird table.

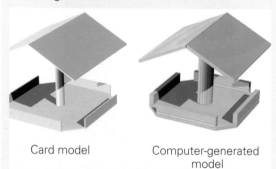

Card model   Computer-generated model

Figure 1.37

(a) Give two reasons why designers would use modelling as part of the design process.
(b) Give two advantages of using a card model.
(c) Give two advantages of using a computer-generated model.

1.10 PRODUCTION PLANNING

When a final design has been completed, the next stage of the design process is planning exactly how the product is to be made. Recording all the stages and the order in which they are to be carried out is called production planning. At this stage you will also have to consider carefully whether you will need to make any control devices to help with the production of your product.

Writing a production plan

A good production plan will include a list of the stages of making the product, in order, and the tools and equipment to be used. It will also highlight any safety hazards at each stage and give an estimate of how long each stage will take. It is important to record when quality-control checks are needed. This information can be shown using tables, flow charts and a Gantt chart.

Tables
The best way to start a production plan is to make a list of all the stages needed to make each part of the product you are making and then put them into a table, using the headings shown in Table 1.3.

Flow charts
The stages of making a component can now be put into a flow chart, and quality-control checks can be added where they are needed. Examples of quality control are:

- checking if a piece of material has been cut to the correct length
- checking if a joint fits together properly
- checking if a piece of wood has a smooth surface, after a sanding operation.

Stage no.	Description of stage	Tools and equipment	Safety	Time
1	Cut 6 mm rod to length	Hacksaw		10 mins
2	Face off in the lathe	Metalwork lathe	Wear goggles No loose clothing	

Table 1.3 A production planning table

Order of Operations

This is the order I produced my product in:

Stage	Materials used	Tools used	Safety Precautions	Predicted time to complete
Mark wood	12mm MDF 9mm MDF	Pencil, ruler, set square.		10min
Cut wood	12mm MDF 9mm MDF	Circular saw	Goggles, lab coat, nothing hanging out of coat.	20min
Sand wood	12mm MDF 9mm MDF	Glass paper	Goggles, lab coat, keep fingers away from glass paper	10min
Cut edges of wood to an angle of 60°	12mm MDF 9mm MDF	Circular saw	Let teacher use, goggles, lab coat	20min
Drill holes in sides	9mm MDF	Screw driver, drill bit-2.5mm	Goggles, lab coat, keep tie in lab coat.	30min
Counter sink holes	9mm MDF	Drill, counter sink	Goggles, lab coat, keep tie in lab coat.	20min
Attach sides to base	12mm MDF 9mm MDF	Screw driver, screws, wood glue	Goggles, lab coat	20min
Attach top shelf to sides	12mm MDF 9mm MDF	Screw driver, screws, wood glue	Goggles, lab coat	20min
Sand wood	12mm MDF 9mm MDF	Glass paper	Lab coat	10min

Drill 25mm diameter holes in top shelf	12mm MDF	Drill, 25mmØ drill bit	Lab coat, goggles	15min
Attach thin black acrylic to sides	9mm MDF 2mm Acrylic	Double sided sticky tape	Lab coat	10min
Drill holes in mirror	Plastic mirror	Drill, 25mmØ drill bit	Lab coat, goggles	15min
Attach mirror to top shelf	12mm MDF Thin plastic mirror	Double sided sticky tape	Lab coat	10min
Spray paint ends and inside	MDF	Black spray paint, black primer	Lab coat, mouth mask	15min
Attach CD cut wood to sliding shelf	12mm MDF	Screw Driver, screws	Lab coat, goggles	20min
Attach wood to middle of sliding shelf	12mm MDF	Screw driver, screws, wood glue	Lab coat, goggles	25min
Bend top of triangle	5mm blue acrylic	Heat strip bender	Lab coat, goggles, be careful wire gets very hot	10min
Cut ends of top triangle	5mm blue acrylic	Ban saw, circular sander	Lab coat, goggles	20min
Attach top triangle to rest of triangle	5mm blue acrylic	Super glue	Lab coat	15min
Cut out groove in sliding shelf	12mm MDF	Router	Lab coat, goggles	15min
Drill hole in bottom of triangle		Screw driver, drill bit	Lab coat, goggles	15min
Insert wooden rod into bottom of triangle	5mm wooden rod		Lab coat	10min

Figure 1.38 Completed production planning tables

Beginning or end

Process

Decision

Figure 1.39 Flow chart symbols

Use ovals to start and end a flow chart, rectangles for descriptions of each stage and diamonds for quality-control checks.

Gantt charts

This is a time plan showing how long each stage of making the product will take and when that stage will be completed. The stages are listed down the left-hand side and timing is plotted across the top. The timing can be plotted in a number of different ways, for example, using dates, weeks, lessons or hours. This chart will show you how long

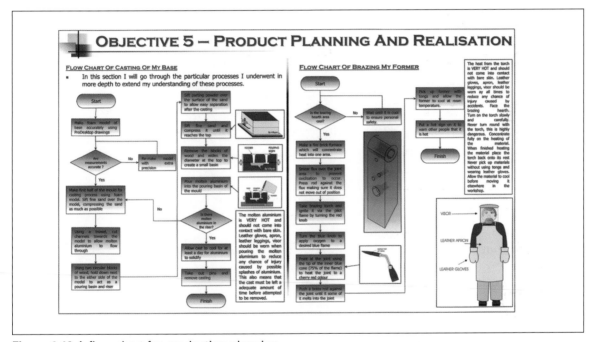

Figure 1.40 A flow chart for production planning

STAGE	LESSONS										
	1	2	3	4	5	6	7	8	9	10	11
Mark wood to length	■										
Cut wood to length		■									
Mark out joints			■	■							
Cut joints					■	■	■				

Table 1.4 A Gantt chart

your project will take to make. It can be used while you are making your product to make sure your work will be finished on time.

▶ Quality control and quality assurance

Control devices

Control devices are made to enable one product to be made to a very high standard, or to enable multiple copies of a product to be made quickly and easily. Examples of control devices are:

- a pattern to be used in a vacuum-forming machine
- a pattern from which a sand casting could be made
- a stencil
- a template
- a jig (for drilling, bending, assembly, etc.).

If a control device is needed to enable your product to be made, you will need to plan its manufacture in the same way as outlined previously.

▶ Making a cutting list

Making a full list of all the materials that will be needed to make a product is a very useful part of the planning process. Cutting lists are best presented in the form of a table. If you are preparing timber, it is usual to add an extra 10 mm for the length and 5 mm for the width, to allow for final planing and trimming to length. Similarly, when cutting metal rod or similar sections of metal or plastic, 3 mm is usually added to allow for final trimming using a metal turning lathe or other similar techniques. The diameter column is useful for round sections such as metal rod, dowel or plastic tube.

Note that 'N/A' for 'not applicable' can be entered in the grid where no measurement needs to be listed.

QUESTION

Figure 1.41 shows a plastic notelet holder. The notelet holder is produced in quantity by injection-moulding.

Quality control is an important part of manufacturing.

Describe two quality-control checks that could be carried out during the manufacture of the injection-moulded notelet holder.

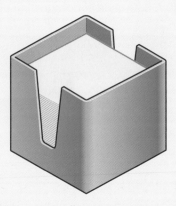

Figure 1.41

Part	No.	Material	Length (mm)	Width (mm)	Thickness (mm)	Diameter (mm)
Sides	2	MDF	210	85	8	N/A
Top	1	Plywood	110	85	6	N/A
Base	1	Plywood	130	85	6	N/A
Connecting rods	6	Mild steel	102	N/A	N/A	8

Table 1.5 A completed cutting list

KEY TERMS

PRODUCTION PLANNING – A step-by-step list of all the stages that need to be carried out to make a product.

CUTTING LIST – A list of all the materials that need to be cut for a product to be made, set out in a table.

QUALITY ASSURANCE – The checks carried out before a product is made and the systems used during manufacture to make sure the product is produced to the required standard.

QUALITY CONTROL – Checks carried out after the product has been made to make sure the product is of the required standard.

1.11 MATERIAL SELECTION

Many products are made up of a number of different components. Each component has a part to play in making the product do its job properly. You will need to consider each component separately, as one material may be ideal for one part but totally unsuitable for another part.

Functional requirements

Selecting the right material can be very difficult and is often one of the most crucial decisions in determining the success or failure of any product. The final decision is often a case of selecting a material with properties that are the best compromise of a number of conflicting requirements. For example, the best material for a component in terms of its strength may be unsuitable because it is too expensive.

One of the first considerations is the environment in which the product is to be used. Many materials deteriorate very quickly when used outside. MDF and chipboard, for example, are unsuitable for outside use. You also need to consider whether a material will fit in with the environment in which the product is going to be used in terms of its appearance.

The demands that will be made on the material in terms of physical properties such as strength and hardness are another important consideration. Some products need to be made from materials that are good conductors of heat or electricity. Other products may have exactly the opposite requirement and need a material that is a very poor conductor of heat or electricity.

Economics

The cost of a material also needs to be considered, particularly for products that are quite large. Small items such as jewellery require a very small amount of material, so expensive materials like gold, silver and diamonds can be used because of their very attractive appearance.

Availability

Most materials are only available in standard forms of supply, such as rod, sheet, tube, bars or even granules. It will be very expensive or even impossible to obtain a material in any other form, so it is vital to select a material that is readily available in the form you need.

Manufacturing method

Some materials are easy to join together; others may be unsuitable for a particular method of production, such as injection-moulding or vacuum-forming. The scale of production is therefore another consideration when selecting a material.

Visual properties of materials and applied finishes

The material you use for each component will have a major effect on the final appearance of the product. For example, sometimes it will be beneficial to use the natural grain of a piece of solid timber, while for other products the perfectly smooth polished surface of a piece of acrylic sheet may be desirable. The appearance of some materials can be changed by using an applied finish like varnish or paint.

Figure 1.42 The visual properties of materials

1.12 CRITICAL EVALUATION SKILLS

The final stage of the design process is to test how well the product does the job it was designed to do. This is done by making an assessment of how well the product performs against each point on the design specification.

❱ Testing

The product needs to be tested by the intended user in its intended location. Ideally, it should be tested in all of the conditions the product will face in its life, including when it is stored and transported, as well as when it is used.

You should devise a series of tests to see how well the product performs against each of the points on the specification. Some points will be very easy to test – for example, if the specification says 'it must weigh less than 2 kg', the test would be to weigh the product. In this case it will be a definite pass or fail. Other aspects will be much more difficult to test – for example, how long the product will last or how easy the product is to use. You will not be able to get a definitive pass or fail; you will only be able to record opinions.

❱ Gathering other people's views on your product

To gather opinions about your product you will need to let a number of people have direct contact with it. The most valuable opinions will be from people who:

- are members of the user group for which the product was designed
- have knowledge about similar products
- have qualifications in aspects of the design being evaluated
- have expertise in using the product being evaluated.

You will need to collect these opinions by conducting interviews with people who have used or tested the product, or by getting these people to fill in a questionnaire.

Testing Product

After making the coffee table, I felt that it was important to test it out to see if it was firstly and most importantly functional and practical. But also to see if it was an effective focal feature in a young couples or young families living room.

From testing the product I found that I was a practical and effective coffee table. It was stable as well as being large enough to place several mugs and plates on to at once. It was also easy to wipe down if any food or drinks were spilt.

It also was an effective storage facility it was easily large enough to store passports, bills and bank documents, as well as any other A4 documents that a young couple or family might want to keep, for example any work documents.

From testing the product I can see that it would be an effective focal point in a young couple's living room despite being fairly small, it looks modern and contemporary. It is a natural finish so would look effective in any coloured living room.

Figure 1.43 A small coffee table being tested

You will need to record the results of your testing by using:

- video, audio and photography records of the testing being carried out
- charts and tables showing clearly the results of testing
- charts and tables showing the strengths and weaknesses of the product.

▶ Recording changes to your final design proposal

You will need to show any changes you have made to your final product proposal and the reasons why these changes were made. If these are minor modifications, this could be done either by showing alterations to the original working drawings or production plan, or by redrafting these documents.

▶ Improving your finished product

You will need to use sketches, drawings and diagrams, showing possible improvements to the product in the light of the testing and evaluation you have carried out. These could be:

- major changes to the overall design of the product
- minor modifications to individual components
- changes to the materials used
- details of changes to the method of manufacture
- changes to the method of construction
- changes to the finish used.

How product could be improved

There are several ways in which my product could be improved and developed further.
  Firstly I could spit one of the draws up into compartments i.e. for bracelets, rings, necklaces… this would enable a young women to store their jewellery more tidily. Even though the tray had compartments in, I feel spilling one of the draws too would improve the product and help the user group.
  Secondly I could use more jigs when making my product, this would enable my product to be more accurate and also easier and quicker to produce identical repeats if this jewellery box was being produced in bulk.
Following on from this, to improve my product I could use machine tools such as an electric sander rather than doing it by hand as this would be much quicker to construct it and there would be less room for error.
  Thirdly I could improve my product by producing identical copies of my jewellery box just varying the type of wood and the finish applied. Even though I think that the wood and finish I chose was the most appropriate and appealing, this would enable young women to decide which would look most effective in their own homes and which would go best with their chosen colour scheme in their bedroom. However this improvement would only be possible if the jewellery box was being produced in bulk.
  Finally I think to improve the quality of my product that on the inside the velvet should go up the sides and not just in the bottom of the draws and the tray. This would keep the jewellery safer and reduce the possibility for scratches occurring even more. In addition to this it would keep the jewellery safer if the women decided to take it on a business trip.

This alteration could be done by wrapping the velvet around the lining and securing with contact adhesive.

Overall however I am exceedingly pleased with the jewellery box I designed as it fulfils my specification completely and incorporates all the preferences I observed when analysing my questionnaire to my user group. It is functional, durable, good value for money and aesthetically pleasing to young women, which was my original aim. Consequently this is a successful design and a successful product.

Figure 1.44 Some details of how a product could be improved

KEY TERM

PRODUCT TESTING – Tests carried out to see how well the product fulfils the design specification.

QUESTIONS

Figure 1.45 shows examples of children's high chairs.

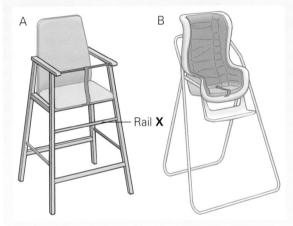

A

B

— Rail **X**

Figure 1.45

1. In use, rail X has been found to be unsatisfactory as a footrest. Sketch a more suitable footrest and show how it is attached to the chair.

2. Describe *two* ways in which the design has considered the safety of the child in high chair A.

3. Give *three* reasons why consumers might choose to buy chair B in preference to chair A.

PRODUCT ANALYSIS

By the end of this chapter you should have developed a knowledge and understanding of:

- the probable specification for the product
- the range of criteria used to analyse a product
- the safety and quality issues involved
- the effect of materials, scale of manufacture and the commercial processes used on the product
- sustainability and environmental issues related to product analysis.

This chapter is about knowing how to analyse a commercial product. Product analysis is about studying how well a product does its job against a range of criteria. It is very important as it will give you a better understanding when researching and looking at existing products and is specifically examined in Question 1 on the examination paper.

2.1 FUNCTION AND/OR PURPOSE OF THE PRODUCT

All products will have a primary function or purpose. Some products will also have a range of secondary functions that make them more successful or appealing products.

The primary function of the computer desk would be to hold the computer and allow the operator to comfortably sit at and use the PC.

Secondary functions of the computer desk may be to store other equipment and accessories such as a printer, files, manuals, CDs, DVDs, etc.

Figure 2.1 Computer desk

Primary functions can be considered as essential if the product is going to be successful; secondary functions are desirable.

The function of the child's toy is to entertain and amuse the child but also to teach important skills for the child's development such as recognising colours, shapes and the development of motor skills when fitting the parts together.

Figure 2.2 A young child's toy

2.2 AESTHETIC APPEAL OF THE PRODUCT

The appearance or look of the product is a very important aspect of product analysis. For many products we buy it is sometimes the most important consideration. When considering the aesthetic appeal of a product we can consider its:

- shape and form
- colour
- texture
- decoration.

Shape and form

The chair shown in Figure 2.3 has a unique form and shape that have been used to create an attractive and interesting solution to the design of a chair.

Colour

Colour is applied to products to make them more interesting and attractive. Changing the colour of a product can drastically change its appearance and often allows the same product to appeal to different types of buyers. Colour can be applied to products with paints, varnishes or coatings, or can be the natural

Figure 2.3 Ross Lovegrove chair

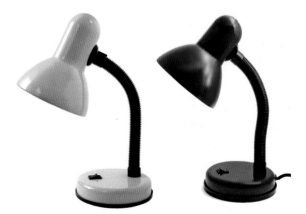

Figure 2.4 Lamps

colour of the material, for example brass, aluminium, oak or acrylic.

▌ Texture

Texture is used on products for many reasons. Texture can make a product more effective, comfortable, appealing, easier to clean, safer or more attractive.

Figure 2.5 **Office chair**

The chair shown has lots of different textures. Consider why different textures are used on the seat, the arm rests and the legs of the chair.

▌ Decoration

Decoration is often added to products to make them more appealing to the customer. Decoration can be applied to a product, such as a pattern, or can be formed from the material itself.

Figure 2.6 **Decorative Clock**

2.3 TARGET AUDIENCE

When analysing products it is important to consider who the product is aimed at. Designers carefully consider their target market when designing new products and may be influenced by such things as age, gender, income, hobbies and interests, cost, lifestyle and image.

When designing a product the designer may also consider other products that would appeal to their target market.

2.4 QUALITY AND SAFETY ISSUES

It is important to consider the quality and safety requirements for products. All products must meet certain safety requirements and this should be an important aspect of any design specification.

A child's toy must be safe for the child to use and will clearly state the age the toy is suitable for. Features the toy would need to have would be no small parts that could cause choking, no sharp edges or finishes, a non-toxic finish and no parts that could trap fingers, etc.

◗ Analysing existing products

Chapters 4 and 5 deal at length with materials, scale of manufacture and commercial processes. It is important that you are able to look at existing products and analyse what they are made out of, the quantity in which they are made and the commercial production method used.

QUESTIONS

Consider how the information about each chair will affect the analysis of the product.

(a) Explain why Chair A is a lot more expensive than Chair B.   [3]

(b) Other than cost, explain **two** advantages of Chair B.   [4]

Chair A	Chair B
Hardwood	Thermosetting plastic
Traditional wood joints	Injection moulded
Made in the UK	Made in the Far East
Batch-produced	Mass-produced
Cost £199	Cost £12

Table 2.1

Chair A

Chair B

Figure 2.7 Garden chairs

2.5 ERGONOMICS AND ANTHROPOMETRICS

When analysing products you should consider ergonomic and anthropometric considerations. Ergonomic considerations could involve a wide range of issues such as ease of use, comfort, safety, texture, colour, smell, etc. Anthropometric considerations might relate to the dimensions of your school chair, for example, so that it is suitable for the range of sizes of the students.

KEY TERMS

ERGONOMICS – The relationship between people and the products they use.
ANTHROPOMETRICS – The study of the sizes of the human body.

2.6 SUSTAINABILITY AND ENVIRONMENTAL ISSUES

Chapter 3 deals with sustainability and the need for designers to be environmentally aware when designing products. When analysing products you should be aware of the environmental and economic impact of the product. Typical issues to consider would be:

- where the product is made (globalisation, labour/production costs)
- the sustainability of the materials used
- the production methods used
- shipping and transport costs
- the typical lifespan of the product (the 'throwaway' society).

2.7 THE PRODUCT SPECIFICATION

Chapter 1 deals with the importance of a design specification. When carrying out product analysis you should consider what the design specification for the product is likely to be.

A design specification is a list of statements that tells the designer *specifically* what the product has to do. The specification will always make reference to the following:

- the function of the product
- the target audience
- what the product will look like
- properties of the materials to be used

- anthropometric and ergonomic considerations
- cost of the product
- production methods
- safety and quality issues
- environmental considerations.

EXAMINER'S TIP

Examination questions will often ask you for specification points for a given product.

QUESTIONS

(a) Before starting to design the computer desk a Design Specification was written. State, with as much detail as you can, what you think was the most important design specification point for each of the following aspects.
   (i) The function or purpose of the computer desk.   [2]
   (ii) The target market for the computer desk.   [2]
   (iii) The safety considerations for the user of the computer desk.   [2]

Figure 2.8 Computer desk

(b) The computer desk is made from laminated chipboard.
State *two* properties that make it the most suitable material for the computer desk.   [2]

(c) The computer desk was made using large-scale production.
Explain why this is the most suitable scale of production.   [2]

CHAPTER 3

SUSTAINABILITY IN DESIGN AND TECHNOLOGY

By the end of this chapter you should have developed a knowledge and understanding of:

- the six Rs of sustainability
- social issues
- moral, ethical and cultural issues
- environmental issues
- design issues
- selection of materials.

As worldwide demand for products and new technology increases, many of the materials used in the production and manufacture of products are running out. Most of these materials are not renewable, so there is great concern that the development of new products and technology is not sustainable and is having a very serious adverse effect on the environment.

This chapter looks at how sustainability and environmental issues, moral and ethical considerations and economic issues influence and affect designing and manufacturing choices and decisions. It provides you with the opportunity to develop a wider understanding of sustainability.

It is very important to look at the world we live in and to consider the needs of future generations. You are encouraged to think about your approach as designers and manufacturers and to consider how we can have a sustainable future.

EXAMINER'S TIP

Question 2 on the examination paper is always about sustainability.

3.1 THE SIX RS OF SUSTAINABILITY

The six Rs of sustainability are some basic principles that have been developed to help ensure the conservation of materials and the protection of the environment.

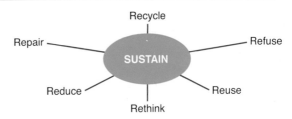

Figure 3.1 The six Rs of sustainability

Recycle	How easy is it to take apart? How can the parts be used again? How much energy will be needed to reprocess parts?
Reuse	Which parts can I use again? Has it another valuable use without processing it?
Reduce	Which parts are not needed? Do we need as much material? Can we simplify the product?
Refuse	Is it really necessary? Is it going to last? Is it fair trade? Is it too unfashionable to be trendy and too costly to be stylish?
Rethink	How can it do the job better? Is it energy efficient? Has it been designed for disassembly?
Repair	Which parts can be replaced? Which parts are going to fail? How easy is it to replace parts?

Table 3.1 The six Rs of sustainability

Figure 3.2 Recycling logo

Recycle

Recycling is what we do with the objects we use in our daily lives. Recycling is the conversion of waste products into new materials, to extend the life and usefulness of a product, item or object that seems to have no further purpose or use once it has been finished with or used for its initial purpose. Recycling means reusing a product but sometimes, before a product can be reused, it will need to undergo processing or treatment.

The three main types of recycling are:

- primary recycling
- secondary or physical recycling
- tertiary or chemical recycling.

Primary recycling

The second-hand use of items – whether clothing-, electronic- or product-based – is a form of primary recycling as the item is simply being used again. Charity shops stock a large selection of recycled products. Giving items to friends and relatives or selling them on internet market sites are all ways of primary recycling.

Figure 3.3 Clothing rail

Secondary or physical recycling

This is the process in which waste materials are recycled into different types of products. The change the product will go through depends on the main fibre or material of the product. Some products can be left to biodegrade before being regenerated into something else. Packaging used for food is often difficult to recycle. However, biodegradable packaging such as 'potatopak' has been developed.

Tertiary or chemical recycling

In this form of recycling, products are broken down and reformulated. For example, plastic bottles can be recycled into fibres and then spun into polyester to make fleece fabric used for coats and blankets. Car tyres can be reused to make numerous products, such as computer mouse mats.

Figure 3.4 Old tyres

ACTIVITY

Carry out some research into biodegradable packaging and look at the advantages and disadvantages of this type of packaging. List the materials the packaging is made from and research alternative materials that it would be possible to recycle.

Figure 3.5 Paper being recycled at a waste-collection plant

Recyclable materials include glass, paper, metals, wood, textiles, electronics, tyres, plastics and food wastes. Most if not all things can be recycled in some way.

Why recycle?

Everything we dispose of goes somewhere, although once the container or bag of rubbish is out of our hands and out of our houses we forget it instantly. Our consumer lifestyle is rapidly filling up rubbish dumps all over the world; as this happens our concerns for the environment grow. When designing and making a new product, designers and manufacturers need to consider how their product can be recycled at the end of its lifespan.

You will need to know about the following for your specific subject/material area:

- materials that can be recycled
- products that use recycled materials
- disassembly – reprocessing materials for use in new products.

Figure 3.6 Recycling – plastic, metal, glass and paper

QUESTIONS

1. What does the term recycling mean?
2. List three products that can be recycled.
3. Name a material made from recycled products.

▶ Reuse

Products that can be reused for either the same purpose or a new purpose

Products that are designed to be reused result in less waste, which leads to conservation of materials and resources. Many places around the UK collect unwanted products or repair them for redistribution for the same or a similar end use.

Products that can be adapted to suit an alternative use

Some local areas have set up their own websites and organisations for the reuse of unwanted items, involving groups of people who actively aim to adapt existing products for alternative uses.

▶ Reduce

Life cycle of a product

A new product progresses through a variety of stages, from the original idea to its decline where it might be discontinued or disposed of. You must consider the impact of a product on the environment and its impact on society as a whole throughout its **life cycle**. The main stages involved are as follows:

- The raw materials – how are they harvested/made?
- The production process – how is the product made?

- Transport and distribution – what, how, where, and how much does it cost?

- Uses – what are the intended uses of the product? How will they be used by the client or the customer?

- Recycling – how can the product be recycled?

- Care and maintenance – what is needed, how much is needed and is it environmentally friendly?

- Disposal – the waste from manufacturing or the product itself. Is it recyclable or biodegradable?

KEY TERM

LIFE CYCLE – The stages a new product goes through, from conception to eventual decomposition.

Eco footprint

The term 'eco footprint' is used to refer to the measurement of our actions on the environment. As a designer, you must consider the effect of your product on the environment, from the first stages of your design ideas to the final making and eventual disposal or recycling of your product. Your footprint involves showing that you have designed the product with the environment in mind and have tried to minimise the damage caused by the various stages throughout your product's life cycle.

Built-in obsolescence

Built-in obsolescence is where the product has been designed to last for a set period of time. The functions of the product have been designed by the manufacturer to fail after a certain length of time. The consumer is then under pressure to purchase again. This built-in obsolescence is in many different products, from vehicles to light bulbs, from items of clothing to food 'use by' or 'best before' dates. Manufacturers can invest money to make the product obsolete more quickly, by making the product with cheaper components, which speeds up this planned obsolescence.

Energy and waste of production process

The consumption of non-renewable energy resources such as coal and oil is causing an energy crisis. These resources will eventually run out. Using non-renewable resources adds to the pollution problem, as products made from oil often take a long time to break down in the environment. Transportation of products is a high user of oil and petrol, which are refined fossil fuels. '**Green energy**' is the name given to alternative energy sources that are considered environmentally friendly and non-polluting. Energy is generated from the following natural sources:

- wind

- solar

Figure 3.7 Wind turbines

- geothermal
- hydro
- tidal/wave.

EXAMINER'S TIPS

The questions below are open-ended questions and your answer should discuss relevant points in the context of your subject/material area.

Use of specialist terms and appropriate use of factual information will allow you to score at the higher mark level.

QUESTIONS

1. Do methods of transportation harm the environment?
2. Are we using too much electricity or too many chemicals that could harm our environment?
3. What alternative sources of energy are available?

Materials – waste

We often overlook how much we waste as consumers, whether it be consumable products, power sources such as electricity or packaging. Waste management is a growing problem, from chemicals that get into the water system, to paper and card used in packaging. Switching off our computers or not leaving the television on standby can help us to reduce the energy we waste. Reusing carrier bags or buying locally made products helps to reduce material waste and bring about a more eco-friendly

footprint. Manufacturers now have to follow guidelines on how to get rid of their waste effluent. Research into effective management of pollution, energy and other material waste is ongoing. You need to be aware of current changes within these areas.

▌ Refuse

Issues relating to sustainable design

Processing, manufacturing, packaging and transport of our products use huge amounts of energy and can create lots of waste. You need to look at the sustainability of a product from an environmental and social viewpoint. How is the product made and can we ensure that no or little harm is introduced into the environment by this method of manufacture? Sometimes a choice between the performance of the product required and the impact on the environment by its manufacture has to be considered and debated.

Materials we should refuse to use

Why should you refuse to use some products? The answer includes a variety of reasons, as set out below.

- The product may be made unnecessarily from man-made instead of natural sources.
- Toxic chemicals may be used in the product.
- The manufacturing process used may mean the product has not been made under safety regulations.
- The product may have been produced by workers who have few rights and work in poor conditions.
- The packaging used may not be good for the environment and the distances and

costs involved in transporting the product may be high.

- It might not be good for you – for example, a food with a high fat content.

You should think about these issues before you accept a product and, above all, do not buy it if you do not need it!

Rethink

Consider your lifestyle and that of others close to you. Think about how you buy products and the energy required to use them. Society is constantly evolving and changing and you can evaluate how you could make a difference.

- How it is possible to approach design problems differently? What ideas can you develop to ensure a difference?

- What could you design using an existing product that has become waste, to use the materials or components for another purpose, without processing the product?

ACTIVITY

1. In groups, discuss what makes you want to buy a product.

2. Discuss and consider what you have bought recently and why. Did you really need it?

Repair

Today's throwaway society means it is quicker and easier to throw something away than to repair it. We looked at built-in obsolescence earlier in this chapter, where manufacturers encourage consumers to repurchase rather than repair.

- Some products you can repair yourself; others have to be taken to repair shops.

- Some products are beyond repair or would cost too much to fix.

- Unwanted electronic and electrical equipment is the fastest-growing waste area. Why? The need to change attitudes in this area is enormous. How can this be achieved?

KEY TERMS

ECO FOOTPRINT – Refers to the measurement of our actions on the environment.

BUILT-IN OBSOLESCENCE – Where a product has been designed to last for a set period of time. The product's functions have been designed by the manufacturer to fail after a certain length of time.

GREEN ENERGY – Alternative energy sources that are considered environmentally friendly and non-polluting.

3.2 SOCIAL ISSUES

Figure 3.8 Logo depicting global unity

Today we live in a global society. You need to be aware of the ways this can affect the designing of products. Products need to be designed for use by a range of different cultures and nationalities, all of which may have different specific needs. Society has become multicultural and diverse; some products may be designed for a specific section of society, while others may be universal.

Social issues include:

- social development through recognising the need to consider the views of others when designing and discussing designed products
- understanding the relationship between man and the general environment
- the economic development cycle of a range of products and the impact on individuals, societies and countries
- issues associated with economic development and employment – where a product is made, costs of components, materials, manufacturing (including labour) and the transportation of the finished product
- the values of society – for example, why we wear clothes: protection, modesty, adornment. Clothing has become a way of reflecting our gender, culture and religion. Some items have become unisex and suitable across society.

3.3 MORAL, ETHICAL AND CULTURAL ISSUES

KEY POINT

- Moral and ethical issues are concerned with the way in which products are manufactured and how they affect the safety, comfort and well-being of people who make them and those who come into contact with the designs/products. Many companies now try to ensure their products are made in the right conditions, without exploiting workers, and to follow a code of practice.

Moral and ethical issues

Moral issues include:

- moral development – reflecting on how technology affects the environment, and the advantages and disadvantages of new technologies to local and national communities such as genetically modified (GM) foods, production automation and manufacture in developing economies

- working conditions within a manufacturing environment, for example job satisfaction, wages, safety of the workplace and workers.

The **Ethical Trading Initiative** (ETI) is an alliance of companies, non-governmental organisations (NGOs) and trade union organisations, whose aim is to promote and improve the implementation of regulated codes of practice that set out minimal working requirements. (See www.ethicaltrade.org for more information.)

Ethical companies ensure that their employees have basic labour rights; they are also careful to protect the environment in the production, packaging and distribution of their goods. Ethical companies are often termed 'sweatshop-free'. '**Sweatshop**' is a term used to describe a business with poor working conditions.

Fairtrade

The Fairtrade Foundation is an independent non-profit organisation that licenses the use of the 'FAIRTRADE Mark' on products in the UK, which meet internationally agreed Fairtrade standards set by Fairtrade Labelling Organisations International (FLO). Products carrying the FAIRTRADE Mark include chocolates, bananas, cotton and beauty

Figure 3.9 The FAIRTRADE Mark

products. Fairtrade ensures farmers and workers in developing countries get a fair and stable price as well as an added premium to invest in their communities. The Foundation was established in 1992. (See www.fairtrade.org.uk for more information.)

Cultural issues

Culture is about the way that people behave and relate to one another. It is about the way that people live, work and spend their leisure time. It is about people's beliefs and aspirations.

KEY TERMS

ETHICAL TRADING INITIATIVE (ETI) – An alliance of companies, non-governmental organisations and trade union organisations that promote and improve the implementation of codes of practice that set out minimal working requirements.
SWEATSHOP – A business with poor working conditions.
CULTURE – The way that people behave and relate to one another; the way that people live, work and spend their leisure time; people's beliefs and aspirations.

Many cultures have important traditions that form part of their identity. How do products affect the quality of lives within different cultures? The use and maintenance of traditional skills and cultural knowledge can have an impact on modern products.

Cultural issues include the following:

- considering, responding to and valuing the responses of others to design solutions
- the impact of different cultures on modern products – the use and maintenance of traditional skills and knowledge.

3.4 ENVIRONMENTAL ISSUES

In a modern, fast-changing society, where products are continually being altered, it is important that you keep up to date with various environmental issues and the impact that products have on the environment. You will need to address the following key points in resistant materials:

- Understand and be able to select materials that are both suitable and sustainable.
- Be aware of the disposal and recycling of materials and components and the appropriate methods of manufacture.
- Prepare materials economically, minimising waste and using pre-manufactured standard components.
- Have knowledge of the reduction in common usage of environmentally unfriendly chemicals and materials dangerous to the environment, such as bleaches, CFCs and toxic materials. The pollution caused by manufacturing can be high, and ways to reduce this are being investigated. It is sometimes necessary to use chemicals and man-made materials that are not the most ecologically sound if the specific performance characteristic of that chemical/material can only be obtained that way.

CFCs

CFCs are one of a group of synthetic substances containing chlorine and bromine, developed in the 1930s. Thought to be safe, non-flammable and non-toxic, they were widely used until the 1980s, when it was discovered that they were the main source of harm to the ozone layer.

Carbon footprint

Carbon footprint is a measure of the impact human activities have on the environment in terms of the amount of greenhouse gases produced through the outlet of carbon dioxide. This has an impact on global warming. A carbon footprint is linked to the ecological footprint and can be measured through transportation of materials and goods, energy use in manufacture, and the use of natural resources and renewable resources.

Figure 3.10 Carbon footprint logo

Carbon offsetting

Carbon offsetting is a method by which people and companies can undertake measures to offset the impact they have on the environment in terms of their carbon footprint. Carbon offsetting involves contributing to the development of more ecological methods of energy generation, such as the use of renewable sources.

Reforestation

The term 'reforestation' is used to describe the restocking of existing forests and woodlands. The advantage of this method is that the areas restocked can provide the ecosystem with resource benefits to soak up some of the negative effects of carbon dioxide.

End-of-life disposal

This issue is linked to the need to dispose of redundant products and their packaging in a safe and environmentally friendly way. The use of labelling for specific packaging is helpful to the consumer when buying products.

Symbols used in resistant materials

Figure 3.11 Symbols used in resistant materials

KEY TERMS

CFCs – One of a group of synthetic substances containing chlorine and bromine that were widely used until the 1980s. They have now been banned since it has been discovered they were the main source of harm to the ozone layer.

CARBON FOOTPRINT – A measure of the human impact on the environment in terms of the amount of greenhouse gases produced through the release of carbon dioxide.

CARBON OFFSETTING – Ways in which individuals and companies can offset the impact they have on the environment in terms of their carbon footprint. It involves contributing to the development of more ecological methods of energy generation.

REFORESTATION – The restocking of existing forests and woodlands.

3.5 DESIGN ISSUES

Researching products

Buying a product can be expensive, so you need to ensure that you have chosen well and that it will benefit you in some way. Researching the product beforehand and analysing the information gathered can help you to come to a conclusion to ensure that your choice is successful.

ACTIVITY

1. Identify how good design and product choice improve quality of life.

2. Look at the way that designers respond to changing styles, tastes, technological advances and environmental pressures. What impact does this have?

QUESTIONS

1. How do you decide when to update your clothes or other products?

2. Why do you want to buy the latest mobile phone?

Designers are constantly changing and evolving their work. Sources of inspiration come from all areas of design and technology. In all products, new and constantly changing materials are being developed. In all the subject areas, smart materials have developed significantly over the last few years. To help you stay up to date in these areas, it would be useful to visit some of the following websites:

- www.voltaicsystems.com – new fabrics made from recycled soda bottles for solar bags
- www.geofabrics.com – fabrics used in landfill, earthworks, railway tracks and drainage
- www.seeitsafe.co.uk – hygienic protection against harmful bacteria in a range of products
- http://tinyurl.com/yrmgfs – sustainable fashion, fashion for the future
- www.ttf.co.uk – timber trade federation to protect the interests of the wood industry
- www.fsc-uk.org – management of long-term timber supplies
- www.bpf.co.uk – leading trade association for the British plastics industry
- www.c4s.info – centre for sustainability
- www.wasteonline.org.uk – recycling of many different materials
- www.recyclemetals.org – BMRA (British Metals Recycling Association)
- www.design-technology.info/alevelsubsite – click on the link 'Smart materials and their uses'
- www.designinsite.dk – click on the 'Environment' link.

Eco-design

This involves the whole system of looking at an end product, from design to finished article, and its use of materials and energy.

Eco-design is the process of designing a product from scratch with the environment in mind, and trying to minimise the damage caused to the environment by the product's life cycle. A designer must think through the following main stages if the product is to be successful and acceptable as eco-designed:

- product planning
- product development
- design process
- functionality
- safety
- ergonomics
- technical issues and requirements
- design aesthetics.

EU Ecolabel

The EU Ecolabel is an official label awarded to a product guaranteeing it has fulfilled specific criteria. A product awarded the EU Ecolabel will have been found to have a smaller environmental impact than other similar products. The EU Ecolabel is the official sign of environmental quality. It is run by the European Commission – along with the key stakeholders – and awarded by independent certification organisations. It is valid throughout Europe. The label's criteria aim to limit the environmental impact of a product over its entire life cycle by looking at such issues as energy and water consumption, waste production and use of renewable resources.

Globalisation of products

The globalisation of products is the internationalisation of products, labour and skills. Products are made in countries where specific traditions, skills and techniques that are part of people's everyday lives can offer valuable income and jobs to a previously poor area. Manufacturers can take advantage of low labour wages. Different cultures may have very different needs.

ACTIVITY

1. Working in a group, list the advantages and disadvantages you would need to be aware of when manufacturing products abroad. Remember to consider the availability of different materials, local culture and working conditions for local workers.

2. Try to list six examples of products that you know have been manufactured abroad.

Figure 3.12 European Ecolabel

3.6 SELECTION OF MATERIALS

KEY POINT

- The extraction and processing of raw materials use massive amounts of energy and produce atmospheric pollution in the form of greenhouse gases. In addition to this, large quantities of waste are produced, causing destruction of wildlife habitats and visual pollution of the environment. Manufacturing uses large amounts of energy and produces much of the waste and pollution, and the effects of **globalisation** also result in excessive usage of fuel and energy to transport materials and products around the world.

Figure 3.13 Environmental effects of manufacturing

Designers and manufacturers have a big part to play in improving sustainability and protecting the environment. The design of products should be carefully considered to find ways of reducing the amount of raw materials used and increasing the use of more environmentally friendly materials. The choice of material to be used for any new product is of great importance, particularly if the product is to be mass-produced.

Advancements in technology and manufacturing processes allow manufacturers to reduce the amount of energy used, and the government's Environment Act places legal requirements on industry to control environmental pollution.

The six Rs of materials

Recycle

Many materials can be recycled, and **recycling** is increasing. Using recycled materials not only cuts down the amount of raw material used, but also reduces the amount of energy needed to process the material. The most common materials to be recycled are glass, paper, plastic bottles and metal cans, and all local councils have recycling facilities for these. To help in the sorting and recycling of plastics and metal cans, symbols giving details of the material are printed or embossed on the products during manufacture. It is hoped that, eventually, all plastic and metal used in products will be recyclable.

As well as the common examples mentioned above, many other items are also recycled,

H D P E

Plastics

Aluminium

RECYCLABLE STEEL

Steel

Figure 3.14 Recycling symbols

often on a very large scale. All metals are in high demand, and as the amount of metal ore available decreases, so the cost rises, making recycling vital if metal production is to continue. Aluminium is the best-known example of a recyclable metal as it is so widely publicised. Recycling aluminium consumes 20 times less energy than extracting the metal from its ore (bauxite), and even with the cost of collecting and sorting, it is still cost effective. With millions of aluminium drink cans used every day, and so much aluminium needed to manufacture products, recycling the metal provides many benefits to manufacturers and to the environment.

Figure 3.15 Metal for recycling

We do not often consider wood to be a recyclable material and often waste wood is burnt or sent to landfill, where it biodegrades. Over recent years, more emphasis has been placed on the recycling of waste wood as a means of reducing the overall use of natural timber. By far the biggest user of wood is the construction industry, and much waste is produced in the form of offcuts and timber from the demolition of old buildings. A lot of wood is also used in packaging, particularly for pallets used to transport materials and

products around the world. Waste wood is recycled by shredding it into fine particles, mostly for use in the manufacture of chipboard and MDF. Other uses include landscaping products (wood chippings), animal bedding materials and as a renewable fuel source for biomass power stations.

ACTIVITY

The tables and benches shown in the photograph have been made from recycled plastic.

Figure 3.16

Find examples of other products that have been made from recycled wood, metal and plastic, and keep details of the products and materials used in your notes. You will find plenty of information on recycling of materials on the internet.

Reuse

For many years we have been known as a 'throwaway' society and many products have been designed to be **disposable**. Good examples of this are packaging, food containers and drink cups. Although most of these products are made from plastics, they are not normally recycled because of problems with contamination and collection. The 'bag for life' sold by many supermarkets is a good example of a product designed for reuse, particularly as it helps to cut down on the number of plastic carrier bags being used and thrown away. Although material is used to produce the bag in the first place, it will outlast hundreds of carrier bags that can cause damage to the environment and wildlife.

Consumables, including food products, are now often marketed in containers that can be reused by the consumer, either for the same purpose or for something entirely different, like storage or display. Containers can be redesigned to improve their appearance (aesthetics) and to encourage people to reuse them.

Reduce

Many products have traditionally been made using much more material than is actually needed. Examples of this are machines that were made using heavy iron castings to make them strong, and wooden beams in buildings that were made from thick sections of timber. In addition to the amount of material used, a great deal of energy is used to produce the products in terms of the heat needed to melt the cast iron and the power needed to saw through the thick wood.

With raw materials in short supply, we need to reduce the amount of material used by products and this can often be done by redesigning the product, or parts of it. Sometimes the product can be redesigned to be made from a different material that is easier to obtain or recycle, or the structure of the product can be altered so that it uses less

Figure 3.17 Milling machine and beams

material to begin with. Where less material is used, the amount of energy needed to make a product is also reduced. Figure 3.18 shows a moulded plastic connecting block. Instead of making the block strong by using thick sections, a series of 'ribs' has been included in the moulding to stop it buckling during use. The mould for this would be slightly more expensive to make, but with every block made, 80 per cent of the plastic needed for the thicker section would be saved.

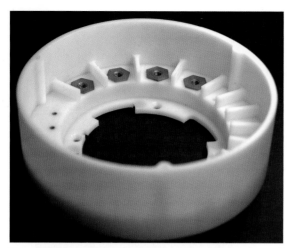

Figure 3.18 Reducing the amount of material used

Refuse

Where materials are in particularly short supply, or the environment is likely to be badly damaged by extracting raw materials, the only solution is to refuse to use the materials. Designers (and, to some extent, manufacturers) have a great influence on sustainability by specifying only materials that are in plentiful supply and whose extraction does not involve the destruction of environmentally sensitive areas. The use of tropical hardwoods, such as teak, has brought about the destruction of large areas of rainforest, further adding to greenhouse gas emissions. In addition, many rainforest trees are ripped out to make way for palm tree plantations in order that the palm oil may be used as a biofuel. Continued use of these materials is not sustainable and alternative materials need to be used to prevent irreversible damage to the environment.

Consumers as well as designers can play their part by refusing to buy products that are made from materials that are not **sustainable**. This could have the effect of causing manufacturers to use other materials, and many companies now advertise their products as having been made using recycled and recyclable materials.

Rethink

There are many ways in which a designer can 'rethink' a product to make it better or more acceptable. Many products are simply updated versions of an existing product, either to improve it or to increase its appeal to the consumer. Changes can be kept to a minimum, while at the same time thinking how material and energy usage can be reduced. Often new technologies and processes can be used that will allow the product to be made with either less material or a different material altogether. Sometimes a whole new concept can be applied to the design of the product, such as with the 'wind-up' torch shown in Figure 3.19, which uses human rather than electrical energy to charge it. This new concept has meant that fewer disposable batteries are used, and the LEDs that provide the light last much longer than normal bulbs, as well as being brighter.

Figure 3.19 Old and 're-thought' torches

Repair

In our throwaway society, large numbers of products are disposed of when something goes wrong with them. Many products are sealed units that cannot be taken apart without destroying the casing, making repair impossible. Because most products are quick to make and quite cheap to buy, it is not considered to be worth spending time or money repairing them, so they are simply thrown away. Not only does this mean that landfill sites fill up more quickly, but also the materials and components used to make the product are wasted, and more material is used to make replacements. A simple redesign of a product's casing could often make repair possible and extend the life of the product considerably.

Life cycle analysis

Life cycle analysis (LCA) is a method used to measure and evaluate the impact of a product across a wide range of environmental issues. LCA involves the collection and analysis of complex data relating to the inputs and outputs of material, energy and all forms of waste. This is carried out over the full life cycle of the product – from raw material extraction and processing, right through to the final end-of-life disposal of the product. It is often referred to as a 'cradle-to-grave' study.

By studying the LCA of a particular product, it is possible to see which stage in the product's life cycle causes most damage to the environment. This will allow a designer to concentrate on that particular aspect when carrying out a redesign of the product. For example, the LCA of a normal family car will show that most environmental damage is caused during the time of the car's use. This has led to the development of more fuel-efficient engines and the search for alternative forms of fuel for vehicles. In other cases it may be found that the extraction of the raw material for a product is the most environmentally damaging part of the life cycle, so a designer will consider using a different material for the product.

Design for disassembly

In recent years there has been much concern expressed over environmental issues relating to manufacturing, and regulations have been put in place to ensure control of industrial pollution. It is becoming increasingly obvious that the disposal of products also causes environmental problems, and manufacturers are being forced to become more responsible for the safe disposal and recycling of used products. Governments are gradually passing laws to cover these issues, such as the End-of-Life Vehicles (ELV) and Waste Electrical and Electronic Equipment (WEEE) directives.

The safe disposal of used products involves ensuring that as much material as possible is recycled or reused and that no potentially dangerous substances are allowed to cause pollution to the environment. To make this happen, products need to be easy to take apart and dismantle, and designers are being encouraged to 'design for disassembly'. This often involves changing the construction of a product and the methods used to hold parts in place, but it can also result in the design

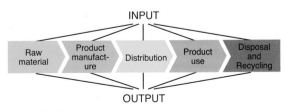

Figure 3.20 Product life cycle

being simplified and therefore using fewer materials and components. One advantage to the manufacturer is that if a product is designed to be easy to disassemble, it could also be easier to assemble in the first place.

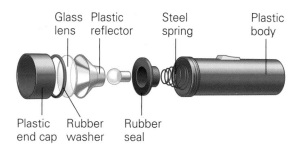

Glass lens   Plastic reflector   Steel spring   Plastic body

Plastic end cap   Rubber washer   Rubber seal

Figure 3.21 Disassembled product

Once the product has been disassembled, all the parts are sorted for recycling, reuse or safe disposal. Although this may be time consuming and expensive, if it is done on a large scale, the savings in materials and reused components, together with the environmental benefits, make it economically viable.

▶ Limited product lifetime

Disposable products, such as packaging, single-use razors, carrier bags and food containers, are designed to be used only once and therefore to have a very limited life. These items are normally more basic in terms of design and quality than other products and they also use less material.

Many products have been produced using the principle of planned obsolescence, meaning that they have been designed to have a limited life and become **obsolete** after a certain period of time. This principle has been applied to consumer durable products (goods for domestic use which should last a

reasonably long time) but which have instead been designed to wear out and need replacing with new products. Improvements in materials and manufacturing technology have resulted in products lasting much longer than they used to, and many manufacturers are now more concerned with building brand loyalty by producing higher-quality products. Fashion trends and design changes now often limit a product's life, but this is because it becomes less appealing to consumers rather than actually being obsolete, as the product can still be used.

Figure 3.22 'Limited life' products

KEY TERMS

DISPOSABLE – Something designed for very limited use.
GLOBALISATION – The manufacture of products in different parts of the world.
RECYCLING – Collecting and processing materials so that they can be used again.
SUSTAINABLE – Able to continue.
OBSOLETE – Unusable or out of date.

KEY POINTS

- Sustainable design is a world issue and one that is constantly changing. We all want the world to be a great sustainable place in which to live – for you, your friends and relatives and future generations.

- A sustainable way of designing can have an impact and a positive effect on everyone. As a designer, you need to remember and consider the social, economic and environmental implications of your decisions.

CHAPTER 4

COMMERCIAL MANUFACTURING PRACTICES

By the end of this chapter you should have developed a knowledge and understanding of:

- commercial manufacturing systems, including one-off, batch and high-volume production
- management systems used for the production of quality commercial products
- the impact of global commercial production
- the environmental impact of commercial production methods
- basic commercial production methods and how they are applied to the manufacture of products
- factors affecting the choice of production method to be used
- the impact of new technologies on industrial production.

This chapter deals with how industry works and the commercial manufacture of products on a large scale. It is important to appreciate that many of the manufacturing processes we use in school are the same as those used in industry.

Because improvements in manufacturing technology are constantly being made, many of the methods and systems we look at may be modified or combined to suit particular situations, especially when the scale of production is very high. Manufacturers have to ensure that their products are made as efficiently and as cheaply as possible, and this often leads to systems being developed specifically for one particular product.

EXAMINER'S TIP

Question 4 on the examination paper will test your knowledge of commercial manufacturing practices.

4.1 COMMERCIAL MANUFACTURING PROCESSES

When learning about manufacturing processes it is important to consider their commercial application as most are used in industry for producing many of the products we use every day. When looking at manufacturing processes it is important to understand:

- the materials used
- the commercial products produced
- the scale of production.

4.2 COMMERCIAL PRODUCTION METHODS

Methods should not be confused with processes. What we do to a material in order to make something is called a process; a method is how we apply that process to manufacture one or more products. The three basic production methods are generally referred to as:

- **one-off production** – sometimes called 'job' production and used for one product or a small number of products
- **batch production** – used to produce a specified quantity of identical products (the number of products in the 'batch' is dependent on many factors, but the batch can be repeated when required)
- **high-volume production** – producing very large numbers of one type of product (the products involved may or may not be identical in every way)
  - The choice of production method to be used is based on the type of product and the quantity to be made.

One-off production

As the name suggests, this method is normally used where only one product is to be specially made, and most of the project work you do in the school workshop will be one-off production. It can also be applied to a small number of products that need to be produced but where it would be too expensive to make special tools to produce them. One-off production is very time consuming and **labour intensive**, often needing highly skilled workers to make all or part of the product, and this makes it an expensive method of production. One advantage of one-off production is that the product is unique and 'hand-made', which often is an indication that the product is of a higher quality than products made in large quantities.

Figure 4.1 A 'one-off' product

Batch production

Batch production is used where a number of identical products are made, and special tools are normally used to make them. The size of a batch of products can be anything from ten to many thousands, depending on a number of factors, but batches can be repeated at any time to make more of the same product.

We can work on a type of batch production in the school workshop by allocating particular tasks to different members of a team. To make a batch of simple metal nameplates, for instance, a team of four people could divide up the tasks as follows:

- Mark out the shape of the nameplate – team member A.
- Saw off the nameplate blank – team member B.
- File the nameplate to shape – team members C & D (two because it takes longer to do).
- Drill the holes in the nameplate – team member A (having done all the marking out).

In this way, a batch of nameplates could be made more quickly than if the team members carried out all the tasks individually.

In industry, batch production is the most widely used production method and virtually all component parts for products are made in this way. Production processes such as injection-moulding, extrusion, presswork and die-casting lend themselves well to batch production, as the tools for making a particular part are made as a self-contained unit (**toolset**). The tools for making one part can be removed from the machine and replaced by a different set of tools quite easily, so one machine can produce many different parts. The toolsets are carefully stored and maintained to use for further batches, and can produce many thousands of identical parts as and when required. Even though the tools cost a lot to make, that cost is spread over the total number of parts made, so the more parts that are made, the cheaper each part can be.

Figure 4.2 Tools for batch production

Table 4.1 shows how the cost of making parts goes down as the number of parts made increases. This is usually referred to as **economy of scale**. The fixed cost is the cost of making the tools and fitting them into the

Number of parts made	1,000	2,000	5,000	10,000
Fixed cost (£)	2,000	2,000	2,000	2,000
Variable cost (£) @ 50p per part	500	1,000	2,500	5,000
Total cost (£)	2,500	3,000	4,500	7,000
Cost per part (£)	2.50	1.50	0.90	0.70

Table 4.1 Economy of scale

machine. The variable cost is the cost of actually making the parts, including material, labour and energy costs. If the parts were made in small batches, the fixed cost would increase to cover the cost of fitting the tools into the machine for each batch.

ACTIVITY

Cut off ten pieces of wood about 20 mm thick (the length and width do not matter). Make a simple jig out of angle iron for drilling two dowel holes in the edge of the piece of wood.

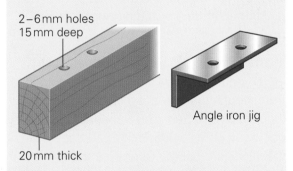

2–6 mm holes
15 mm deep

Angle iron jig

20 mm thick

Figure 4.3

Mark out and drill the two dowel holes in five of the pieces of wood and time how long it takes. Use the jig to drill the two dowel holes in the other five pieces of wood, timing how long it takes.

1. Which five pieces took the least time? Explain why.
2. Which five pieces were done most accurately? Explain why.

High-volume production

This is sometimes referred to as mass production and it refers to the high-volume manufacture of products that may or may not be identical. A lot of specialist equipment is needed and it is very expensive to set up this type of production, meaning that it is only possible to use it if large numbers of products are to be made. The cost of all the special tooling and equipment is offset by the speed and efficiency of production and the fact that only a few skilled workers are needed.

Typical examples of the volume production method of manufacture are cars and domestic appliances such as washing machines. These are produced on automated assembly lines, using computer-controlled handling systems to move materials and component parts, and robots to perform the operations needed to make the product. The system allows slight differences between products to be made during their manufacture, such as different upholstery in a car or a more complex programmer in a washing machine. The computer controlling the system ensures that the right parts required for the product are supplied for assembly at the right time.

Figure 4.4 A production line

KEY TERMS

ONE-OFF PRODUCTION – Making only one product or a small number of products.
BATCH PRODUCTION – Making a set number of identical products.
HIGH-VOLUME PRODUCTION – Producing very large numbers (mass production).
LABOUR INTENSIVE – Requiring a large number of workers to produce a product.
TOOLSET – A self-contained unit of tools for making a particular part during batch production.
ECONOMY OF SCALE – Where the cost of making parts goes down as the number of parts made increases.

4.3 THE IMPACT OF NEW TECHNOLOGIES

KEY POINT

- New technologies such as CAD/CAM, rapid prototyping and computer-controlled machines have enabled products to be developed and produced more quickly.

Industrial applications of CAD/CAM

CAD/CAM is dealt with in more detail in Chapter 8, but both these applications have been developed further for use in industrial production. The use of CAD/CAM in the design and development of new products has resulted in products coming into production faster than was the case using more traditional techniques. On-screen modelling and rapid prototyping, together with the ability to make changes easily, enable a design to be developed quickly. When the final design is chosen, the special tools such as moulds and dies needed to manufacture the product are made directly from the CAD package. All the design details can be shared electronically with companies around the world, enabling the CAM function to be performed wherever the product is to be manufactured.

Instead of using separate machines such as lathes, routers and milling machines for all the manufacturing processes, multipurpose machines have been developed that can carry out many different operations. These machines are usually referred to as **machining centres** and are computer-controlled, often as part of a fully integrated manufacturing system.

Rapid prototyping

CAD packages allow the designer to view a 3D image of a new design on screen, and a number of systems are now available for converting computer-generated designs into solid 3D models. These systems are referred to as **rapid prototyping** systems, all being computer controlled and most being fully automatic. The 3D design is first divided up by computer software into thin horizontal 'layers'. These layers are then sent in sequence to the rapid prototyping system, where the solid model is built up layer by layer.

The 3D models are produced in a number of different ways:

Laminating

One of the earliest systems, **laminating** uses a vinyl cutter to cut individual layers out of adhesive-backed card. The layers are then stuck together to produce the solid model, which can be trimmed and painted to provide the finished prototype. Although the process is rather time consuming, it can be done quite cheaply and can produce models that would be very difficult to make in any other way.

3D printing

This system works in a similar way to an inkjet printer and builds up a 3D model by 'printing' the layers onto the bed of the machine, using either molten ABS plastic, powder or wax. The 'print head' is computer controlled to trace out the shape of the 3D model layer. When the first layer has been printed, the bed of the machine is lowered by an amount equal to the thickness of each layer. The process is then repeated for all the remaining layers until the complete object has been produced.

The materials used in **3D printing** have been developed to enable stronger, fully functioning prototypes to be produced. With continuing developments in materials and processes, 3D printing can be used for the rapid manufacture of products on a one-off or small-batch basis.

Stereolithography

This system is widely used in industry to produce good-quality prototypes from liquid plastic resin. The **stereolithography** machine consists of a tank of liquid resin, a movable platform on which to build the prototype and a computer-guided laser. The laser traces out the shape of a layer of the 3D design onto the surface of the liquid resin in the tank. This cures the resin to the shape required and the platform is then lowered to enable the next layer to be cured on top of the previous one. The process is repeated until all the layers have been cured, to produce the completed 3D prototype.

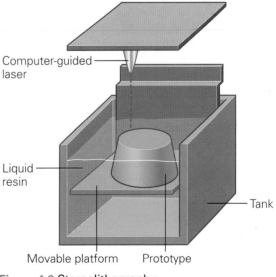

Computer-guided laser

Liquid resin

Tank

Movable platform   Prototype

Figure 4.6 Stereolithography

Figure 4.5 A 3D printer

Laser-sintering

Laser-sintering works in a similar way to stereolithography, but the raw material is a fine, heat-fusible powder, rather than a liquid. The computer-guided laser fuses the surface of the powder in the shape of one layer of the 3D design, and this process is repeated until the prototype is completed, lowering the platform after each layer. The powders used may be plastic, metal, ceramic or a combination of these, which allows prototypes with good impact strength and thermal resistance to be produced.

▶ Just in Time (JIT)

This is a modern manufacturing system developed by Toyota in Japan. Products are assembled and made only when they are required, in the correct quantity and at the correct time. This prevents expensive overproduction of products that do not have customers and allows products to be more easily tailored to the customer's needs, for example the colour and specification.

KEY TERMS

MACHINING CENTRES – Computer-controlled multipurpose machines that can carry out many different operations.
RAPID PROTOTYPING – Making a 3D prototype in layers by computer control.
LAMINATING – Individual layers are cut out of adhesive-backed card using a vinyl cutter to produce a solid model.
3D PRINTER – A printer that makes 3D prototypes out of molten plastic or wax.
STEREOLITHOGRAPHY – Making 3D prototypes by curing liquid resin with a laser.
LASER-SINTERING – Using a laser to fuse fine powders in layers to make a 3D prototype.

4.4 GLOBALISATION

KEY POINTS

- With ever-improving transport and communication links, it is often said that the world is getting smaller. Not only has this allowed manufacturers to sell their products around the world, but it has also enabled them to take advantage of social and economic differences between countries. Many large organisations have become **multinational companies** with factories around the world, where their production facilities can be close to the required raw materials and can also make use of the availability of cheap labour.

In recent years it has become increasingly common for companies to transfer their production to other countries so that they can make their products more cheaply, and in some cases whole factories have been moved to a different country. This has led to a decline in manufacturing in countries such as the UK and Germany, and the rapid industrialisation of previously underdeveloped countries in other parts of the world, which have become known as 'emerging economies', such as Poland, Thailand and India.

In some cases, the cost of labour is not as important as logistical considerations, and many large companies have built new factories in other countries in order to make their products closer to the market in which they are to be sold. Examples of this are the Japanese-owned Nissan factory in Sunderland and the Toyota factory in Derby, where vehicles are produced mainly for the European market.

While globalisation is felt to be both socially and economically beneficial, there are concerns about the treatment of workers in the emerging economies, particularly with regard to the use of young children in manufacturing, and the amount that workers are paid.

Another major concern is the **environmental impact** of transporting materials and goods around the world, and heavily loaded container ships, like the one in Figure 4.7, are a familiar sight in every major shipping port.

Figure 4.7 Container ship

KEY TERMS

MULTINATIONAL COMPANIES – Companies that operate in many different countries.

INDUSTRIALISATION – Increasing the amount of manufacturing carried out in an area or country.

ENVIRONMENTAL IMPACT – The effects of manufacturing on the environment.

CHAPTER 5

MATERIALS AND COMPONENTS

By the end of this chapter you should have developed a knowledge and understanding of:

- the general classification of resistant materials
- performance characteristics of resistant materials
- the conversion of resistant materials into other usable forms
- the finishing processes applied to resistant materials to improve performance and appearance
- smart and modern materials
- form of materials and their selection
- environmental and sustainability issues
- pre-manufactured components.

This chapter deals with a range of resistant materials: wood, metal, plastics and components. It will help you to undertake design and to carry out controlled assessment tasks, and it will prepare you for Question 6 on the examination paper.

In order to make reasoned decisions about resistant materials, you need to consider a number of different aspects, including information about their uses, properties, availability and environmental issues.

5.1 THE GENERAL CLASSIFICATION OF RESISTANT MATERIALS

Woods

There are two families of solid wood:

- **Hardwoods**, such as oak, ash and beech, come from broad-leaved, deciduous trees,

that is, trees that shed their leaves in autumn.

- **Softwoods**, such as pine, come from coniferous (cone-bearing) trees that remain evergreen all year round.

Solid wood has a grain that is stronger along its length than across its width. Softwoods generally have a wider grain than hardwoods and they grow faster. Their speed of growth means that softwoods are generally cheaper than hardwoods.

The terms softwood and hardwood are used to describe the cellular structure of the tree.

It does not mean that hardwoods are necessarily hard or that softwoods are soft. In fact, balsa wood is a hardwood yet it is light and soft, whereas softwoods like yew are heavy and difficult to work with.

Solid woods contain moisture and as they dry out they shrink. This can cause the wood to twist, warp and split.

Name	Source	Properties/working characteristics	Uses
Beech	UK, Europe	Very tough, hard, straight and close-grained, withstands wear and shocks, polishes well, liable to warp	Chairs, flooring, tools, turnery, toys, steam-bent furniture
Ash	UK, Europe	Wide-grained, tough, very flexible, finishes well	Tool handles, sports equipment including cricket stumps and hockey sticks, ladders
Oak	Europe	Heavy, hard, tough, open grain, finishes well, good outdoors, contains tannic acid so will corode steel screws, leaving a blue stain	Boat building, floors, gateposts, high-class furniture and fittings
Birch	Europe, North America	Fine-grained, pale in colour, very suitable for making thin veneer, excellent acoustic properties	Making plywood, music speakers, drums
Mahogany	Africa, South America	Easy to work, wide boards available, polishes quite well, but has interlocking grain that makes it difficult to work	Indoor furniture, shop fittings, veneers used to face manufactured boards
Jellutong	Asia	Low density, straight grain, fine texture, easy to work and shape	Product model making
Teak	Burma, India	Hard, durable, natural oils, resists moisture, fire, acids and alkalis, straight grain, works well, very expensive	Laboratory benches, high-class furniture, veneers, garden furniture, traditional boat decks
Balsa	South America	Very soft but high in strength, the softest commercial hardwood	Model making, centre layer in table-tennis bats, in laminates with glass-reinforced plastic (GRP) in surfboards

Table 5.1 Common hardwoods

EXAMINER'S TIPS

Examiners ask questions about materials in two ways. They either ask you to name a material or they state a material and ask you why it is suitable – for example, 'Name a suitable hardwood for a child's toy', or 'Give a reason why beech is suitable for a child's toy'.

Name	Source	Properties/working characteristics	Uses
Redwood (Scots pine)	Northern Europe, Russia	Straight grain, knotty, easy to work, finishes well, durable; widely available and relatively cheap	Most commonly used for construction work; suitable for all inside work but needs protection when used outdoors
Western red cedar	USA, Canada	Lightweight, knot-free, straight grain, contains natural oils that protect from weather, insects, dry rot; fine silky surface	Outdoor joinery, e.g. cladding of buildings, wall panelling
Parana pine	South America	Hard, straight grain, almost knot-free, available in wide boards	Good-quality inside joinery such as staircases and built-in furniture
Whitewood (spruce)	Northern Europe, Canada, USA	Fairly strong, resistant to splitting, easy to work	General indoor furniture

Table 5.2 Common softwoods

▶ Manufactured boards

Manufactured boards are wood-based materials that are made by compressing and bonding thin sheets of wood, pulp or particles with adhesive.

Advantages of manufactured boards over solid woods

- Manufactured boards are constructed so that they are more stable than solid woods.

- Manufactured boards are available in larger sheet sizes than wood cut directly from trees. Sheets as large as 2440 x 1220 mm can be purchased.

- Manufactured boards are more readily available from do-it-yourself stores and timber merchants than most hardwoods and softwoods.

- Manufactured boards tend to be less expensive than hardwoods and softwoods.

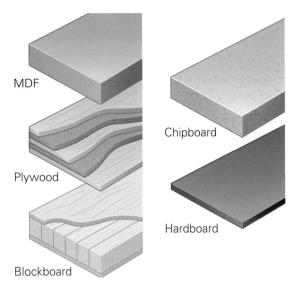

MDF

Plywood

Blockboard

Chipboard

Hardboard

Figure 5.1 Commonly used manufactured boards

MDF

MDF (medium density fibreboard) is made by compressing and gluing tiny particles of wood and fibres together. It has no grain and a very smooth surface. It saws and machines well and can be painted or covered with veneers. It is used to make indoor furniture.

Plywood

Plywood is made by 'laminating' or gluing together a number of layers known as veneers or plies. Each layer is glued to the previous one with the grain running at 90 degrees. This makes a very stable board that is unlikely to bend, twist or warp. So that the grain of the top and bottom layers of the plywood run in the same direction, there is always an odd number of veneers – three, five, seven and so on. There are different grades of plywood used for specific tasks: marine plywood for boat building; a cheap, coarse grade for concrete 'shuttering' in the building industry; and higher-quality plywood used for doors and drawer bottoms in the furniture industry.

Chipboard

Chipboard is made by compressing and gluing wooden chips together. Chipboard can be difficult to work with because it tends to crumble. There are different grades for specific tasks with flooring quality or denser quality used for kitchen surfaces. It is relatively cheap and although it is not very attractive, it can be purchased covered with a tough veneer or plastic coating to improve its appearance.

Hardboard

Hardboard is made by compressing and gluing small wood fibres together. One side of the board is usually smooth, while the other has a rough texture. Hardboard is used for drawer bottoms and the backs of cabinets. When used for larger items such as doors it needs to be fixed to a wooden frame. It can be used as a cheaper alternative to plywood where strength is not important.

 KEY TERMS

HARDWOODS – Wood that comes from deciduous trees such as oak, ash and beech.
SOFTWOODS – Wood from evergreen trees such as pine.
MANUFACTURED BOARDS – Wood-based materials that are made by compressing and bonding thin sheets of wood, pulp or particles with adhesive.

▶ Metals

There are two families of metals:

- **Ferrous** metals, such as steel, contain iron.
- **Non-ferrous** metals, such as aluminium and copper, do not contain iron.

Ferrous metals contain differing amounts of carbon. The amount of carbon added to the iron depends on the type of steel and the properties required. For example, high-carbon steel, used to make drills, files and chisels, contains much more carbon than mild steel, used to make nuts and bolts.

Both ferrous and non-ferrous metals can be subdivided into two further categories:

- **Pure metals** are made from one single element. Examples include aluminium, copper, iron lead, tin, zinc, silver and gold.
- **Alloys** are metals that are a mixture of two or more pure metals with other elements to produce a 'tailor-made' metal with special properties not otherwise available in a single metal.

Metal	Composition	Properties/working characteristics	Uses
Cast iron	Remelted pig iron with additions	Hard skin but brittle soft core; rigid under compression but cannot be bent or forged	Heavy crushing machines, car cylinder blocks, machine parts, vices
Mild steel	Alloy of iron and 0.15–0.30% carbon	High tensile strength, ductile, tough, fairly malleable, poor resistance to corrosion; it cannot be hardened due to low carbon content	General purpose, nails, screws, nuts and bolts, plate, sheet, tube, girders, car bodies
Medium-carbon steel	0.30–0.70% carbon	Stronger and harder than mild steel but less ductile, tough and malleable	Garden tools such as trowels and forks, springs
High-carbon steel	0.70–1.40% carbon	Hardest of the carbon steels; less ductile, tough or malleable	Hammers, chisels, screwdrivers, drills, files, taps and dies
Stainless steel	Alloy of steel with 18% chrome and 8% nickel	Resistant to corrosion, hard, tough; difficult to work	Sinks, dishes, cutlery
High-speed steel	Medium-carbon steel with tungsten, chromium, vanadium	Retains hardness at high temperatures; resistant to high level of frictional heat; can only be ground	Drills, lathe cutting tools
High-tensile steel	Low-carbon steel with nickel and chrome	Extremely hard and tough	Gears, shafts, engine parts, turbine blades

Table 5.3 Common ferrous metals

Metal	Composition	Properties/working characteristics	Uses
Aluminium	Pure metal	Light, soft, ductile, malleable, can be welded, good conductor of heat and electricity, corrosion resistant, polishes well	Aircraft bodies, saucepans, cooking utensils, packaging, foils, cans, window frames
Duralumin	Alloy of aluminium with 4% copper, 1% manganese and magnesium	Equivalent strength as mild steel but much lighter, ductile, machines well, becomes harder when worked	Aircraft and vehicle parts
Copper	Pure metal	Malleable, ductile, tough, good conductor of heat/electricity, easily joined, corrosion resistant; easily soldered	Electrical wire, hot-water tanks, central-heating pipes, printed circuits
Gilding metal	Alloy of 85% copper, 15% zinc	Corrosion resistant, solders easily, attractive golden colour; can be enamelled	Beaten metalwork, jewellery
Brass	Alloy of 65% copper, 35% zinc	Corrosion resistant; heat and electrical conductor, easily joined; casts well	Castings, forgings, ornaments, boat fittings
Bronze	Alloy of 90% copper, 10% tin	Tough, hardwearing, corrosion resistant	Bearings, castings for statues, coins; air, water and steam valves
Pewter	Alloy of at least 90% tin + copper and antimony	Malleable, low melting point	Tableware, statues and figurines, casting
Silver	Pure metal	Highest electrical conductivity of any metal, expensive precious metal	Jewellery, expensive tableware, electrical contacts, used as a solder and brazing alloy

Table 5.4 Common non-ferrous metals

KEY TERMS

FERROUS METALS – Metals that contain iron, such as steel.
NON-FERROUS METALS – Metals that do not contain iron, such as aluminium.
PURE METALS – Metals made from one single element, such as copper, tin, silver and gold.
ALLOYS – A mixture of two or more pure metals with other elements to produce a 'tailor-made' metal with special properties not otherwise available in a single metal.

Plastics

There are two families of plastics:

- **Thermoplastics**, such as acrylic and polythene, can be heated to make them soft so that they can be shaped or formed. When they cool they return to a rigid state. This process can be repeated many times for thermoplastics. **Plastic memory** is the ability of thermoplastics to return to their original state after reheating.

- **Thermosetting plastics**, such as melamine, can also be heated to make them soft to shape and form, but this can only be done once. Thermosetting plastics are particularly useful for making products that need to keep their shape and are resistant to heat.

Different plastics products require different working properties. Substances are sometimes added to the raw material used to make a specific plastic. Plasticisers are added

Common name	Properties/working characteristics	Uses
Low-density polythene	Range of colours, tough, flexible, good electrical insulator and chemical resistance	Washing-up liquid, detergent and squeezy bottles, bin liners, carrier bags
High-density polythene	Range of colours, hard, stiff, good chemical resistance, high impact	Milk crates, bottles, pipes, buckets, bowls
PVCu	Stiff, hard, tough, good chemical and weather resistance	Pipes, guttering, roofing sheets, window frames
High-impact Polystyrene	Range of colours, stiff, hard, lightweight, safe with food, good water resistance	Disposable plates, cups, fridge linings, model kits, food containers
Expanded polystyrene	Lightweight, absorbs shock, good sound and heat insulator	Sound and heat insulation, protective packaging
Nylon	Hard, tough, resilient to wear, self-lubricating, resistant to chemicals and high temperatures	Gear wheels, bearings, curtain-rail fittings, clothing, combs, power-tool cases, hinges
PET	Clear, cheap, food safe, easy to form/mould.	Food containers and packaging
Acrylic	Stiff, hard, clear, durable outdoors, easily machined and polished, good range of colours, excellent impact resistance (glass substitute); does scratch easily	Illuminated signs, aircraft canopies, car rear-light clusters, baths, Perspex™ sheet
ABS	Tough, high-impact strength, lightweight, scratch resistant, chemical resistance, excellent appearance and finish	Kitchenware, safety helmets, car parts, telephones, food mixers, toys

Table 5.5 Common thermoplastics

Common name	Properties/working characteristics	Uses
Urea-formaldehyde	Stiff, hard, brittle, heat resistant, good electrical insulator, range of colours	White electrical fittings, domestic appliance parts, wood glue
Melamine-formaldehyde	Stiff, hard, strong, range of colours, scratch and stain resistant, odourless	Tableware, decorative laminates for work surfaces, electrical insulation
Epoxy resin	Good chemical and wear resistance, resists heat to 250°C, electrical insulator	Adhesive such as Araldite™ used to bond different materials such as wood, metal and porcelain
Polyester resin	When laminated with glass fibre becomes tough, hard and strong; brittle without reinforcement	GRP boats, chair shells, car bodies

Table 5.6 Common thermosetting plastics

to make the plastic very soft and pliable. Dyes and pigments are added to make a particular colour. Fillers are added to increase the 'bulk' of a plastic cheaply.

KEY TERMS

THERMOPLASTICS – Soft when heated, enabling them to be shaped or formed. They return to a rigid state when cool and the process can be repeated many times Examples include acrylic and polythene.
PLASTIC MEMORY – The ability of thermoplastics to return to their original state after reheating.
THERMOSETTING PLASTICS – Plastics that can be heated to make them soft to shape and form, but which can only be done once. They are useful for making heat-resistant products that need to keep their shape. An example is melamine.

EXAMINER'S TIPS

When naming a material, be specific. For example:

- Do not say 'softwood' when the question demands a specific name, for example, 'western red cedar'.
- Do not say 'metal' when you mean 'mild steel'.
- Do not say 'plastic' when you mean 'polypropylene'.

Examiners will not give a mark for 'strong' or 'strength' as a working property for any material unless it is justified. For example, 'high-impact strength', 'tensile strength' or even 'strong enough to support the weight of …' are all answers that give some justification to 'strong' or 'strength'.

ACTIVITY

1. When you are asked to name a specific material for a product, think of it as a task with four separate stages.

   Stage 1: Ask yourself three questions about the product:
   - What does it do?
   - How is it used?
   - Where is it used?

   Stage 2: Ask yourself: What working properties must the material have that is used to make the product?

   Stage 3: Ask yourself: Which family of materials would be most suitable: wood, metal and/or plastics?

   Stage 4: Name a suitable, specific material.

   Try this approach for three different products:
   - a wooden garden seat
   - central-heating pipes
   - the plastic shell for a school chair.

2. Name as many specific materials as you can, used in the construction of a mountain bike.

Figure 5.2 Mountain bike

5.2 · PERFORMANCE CHARACTERISTICS OF MATERIALS

The performance characteristics of a material enable it to meet the demands made of it in a particular situation. For example, when deciding which materials are most suitable for making outdoor furniture, you would want to consider those materials that are resistant to moisture or those that are not too heavy, so that the furniture could be moved easily.

EXAMINER'S TIPS

Examiners will be impressed if you can describe a specific performance characteristic from those below when giving a reason for choosing a material for a particular purpose.

Hardness

Hardness is the extent to which a material will resist cutting and indentations to its surface.

Toughness

Toughness is the extent to which a material can withstand shocks such as hammering. It is the opposite of being brittle.

Tensile strength

Tensile strength includes four different types of strength, including an ability to withstand being:

- pulled apart or stretched
- crushed or compressed
- twisted
- sheared as a result of a sideways force.

Elasticity

Elasticity is the extent to which a material can be stretched and then return to its original length. Every material has an elastic limit. When a material is stretched further than its limit, its shape is changed permanently.

Flexibility

Flexibility is the ability to bend without breaking and then spring back to its original shape. A material that has no flexibility is rigid.

Impact resistance

Impact resistance is the ability to resist sudden shocks.

Strength-to-weight ratio

The strength-to-weight ratio is a measure of the strength of the material compared to its weight. For example, some materials, such as aluminium, which is a lightweight metal, have a very high strength-to-weight ratio, while others, such as zinc, have a poor strength-to-weight ratio.

Ductility

Ductility is the ability to be stretched like a length of wire without breaking.

Malleability

Malleability is the ability of the material to be hammered, rolled or pressed into shape without breaking.

Thermal and electrical conductivity

Thermal and electrical conductivity is the ability to conduct heat and electricity.

Aesthetic qualities

Aesthetic qualities apply to the physical appearance of the material, for example its colour, grain or surface finish.

ACTIVITY

Using the information in Tables 5.1–5.6, draw your own table to carry out the two tasks described below.

1. For each of the following performance characteristics, name two materials that possess that characteristic:
   - hardness
   - toughness
   - tensile strength
   - elasticity
   - flexibility
   - impact resistance
   - strength-to-weight ratio
   - ductility
   - malleability
   - thermal and electrical conductivity
   - aesthetic qualities.

2. Name a different product made from each material.

5.3 FORMS OF MATERIALS AND THEIR SELECTION

Market forms

> KEY POINT
>
> - It would be quite possible for materials to be produced in virtually any shape and size we might want, but they are normally made available in standard forms and sizes to cut down production costs. These standard sizes and sections are known as **market forms**.

You need to know about the standard forms and sizes of different materials that you can use when designing and making, so that you do not waste time and materials having to make them into different shapes or sizes.

Figure 5.3 Market forms

Wood

When a tree is cut down, the branches are cut off and the bark removed from the trunk before it is cut along its length into roughly sawn boards. This is known as **conversion**, and these boards will later be made into the shapes and sizes the wood will be sold in. At this stage we often refer to the wood as **green timber** – this does not mean it is green in colour; it simply means that it still contains a lot of moisture.

Green timber is sometimes used for large sections of wood needed for construction, such as the green oak frames used in some buildings, but normally the timber is dried out, or **seasoned**, before being made into usable forms. This is done by stacking the rough-sawn boards in such a way that air can circulate easily between them and reduce the amount of moisture in the wood. Seasoning can be achieved slowly by allowing the timber to dry out naturally in the air or more quickly by drying the timber in a kiln. Kiln seasoning is more common than air seasoning because it is reliable and easy to control, and because it produces usable timber more quickly.

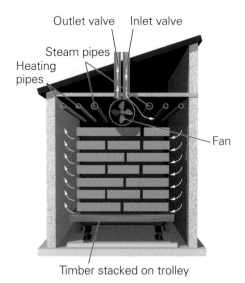

Figure 5.4 Kiln seasoning timber

After conversion and seasoning, the timber is ready to be reduced into the standard shapes and sizes it will be sold in. This is carried out using a wide range of woodworking machinery, including circular saws, bandsaws and planing machines.

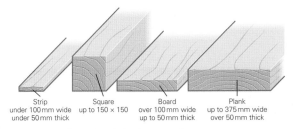

| Strip | Square | Board | Plank |
| under 100mm wide
under 50mm thick | up to 150 × 150 | over 100mm wide
up to 50mm thick | up to 375mm wide
over 50mm thick |

Figure 5.5 Standard timber sections

Rough-sawn timber is often planed to give a smooth surface to the wood. Planed timber can either be planed on both sides (**PBS**) or planed all round (**PAR**), and the planing will make the sizes approximately 3 mm smaller than the (nominal) sawn size. Planed timber is more expensive than sawn timber and is only used where a smooth finish and accurate size are needed.

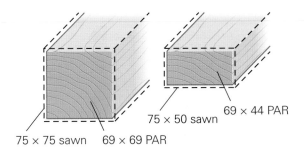

69 × 44 PAR
75 × 50 sawn
75 × 75 sawn   69 × 69 PAR

Figure 5.6 Typical planed timber sizes

As well as all these standard sections of timber, it is now possible to buy wood in other forms to suit particular applications. As manufacturing technology improves, the range of forms available is increasing all the time, and in some cases they have been used to replace the original standard forms.

Timber mouldings are available in many different shapes and sizes and can be used for either construction or decorative purposes. Although they are called mouldings, they are actually made by machining the timber using specially made cutters to produce the shape required. This makes them more expensive than the standard shapes. The wood that is cut away to form the shape of the mouldings is not wasted as it is used in the production of large manufactured boards.

Standard sections

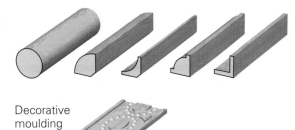

Decorative moulding

Figure 5.7 Timber mouldings

Figure 5.8 Manufactured boards

KEY POINT

- **Manufactured boards** were introduced to reduce the amount of natural timber being used. They are produced in large sheets and are said to be stable as they do not twist and warp like natural timber boards. Much of the material used to make these boards comes from the waste products of timber conversion and machining, making the boards economical as well as useful.

Type of board	Board sizes	Standard thicknesses
MDF	2440 × 1220 mm; 2440 × 607 mm; 1220 × 607 mm	3 mm; 6 mm; 9 mm; 12 mm; 16 mm; 18 mm
Plywood	2440 × 1220 mm	4 mm; 6 mm; 9 mm; 12 mm
Blockboard	2440 × 1220 mm	18 mm
Chipboard	2440 × 1220 mm; 1220 × 607 mm	12 mm; 18 mm
Hardboard	2240 × 1220 mm	3 mm; 6 mm

The smaller board sizes are cut from the standard 2440 × 1220 mm board.
MDF, plywood and chipboard can also be bought with a veneer finish on one or both sides.

Table 5.7 Standard sizes of manufactured boards

KEY POINT

- **Veneers** are thin sheets of wood cut from logs by rotary peeling on a special lathe or by slicing from a long block.

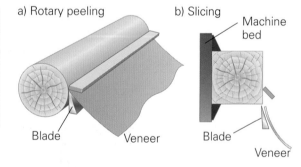

Figure 5.9 Cutting wood veneers

Veneers are used to make plywood and other manufactured boards. Manufactured boards are often covered by veneers to give them a smoother surface and to improve their appearance. A good example of this is the use of expensive hardwood veneers on MDF for making furniture.

KEY TERMS

CONVERSION – The process of removing the branches and bark from a cut-down tree, then cutting it along its length to form roughly sawn boards.

GREEN TIMBER – Wood that still contains a lot of moisture.

SEASON – To dry out excess moisture from newly cut timber.

PBS – Timber that has been planed on both sides.

PAR – Timber that has been planed all round.

TIMBER MOULDING – A length of shaped section machined from natural timber.

MANUFACTURED BOARD – A sheet of wood-based material mostly made from waste timber products.

VENEER – Thin sheets of natural wood.

ACTIVITY

1. Prepare a stock list of the wood materials in your workshop. Present this in the form of a table and include details such as name of timber, type of wood (hardwood or softwood), forms and sizes, type and thickness of manufactured boards, shapes of timber mouldings.

2. Visit your local DIY store and look at the timber for sale there.
   (a) How much difference is there between the price of sawn timber and planed timber?
   (b) Why do you think there is this difference?
   (c) How many different shapes of timber mouldings does the store sell?

❯ Metals

Figure 5.10 Metals

KEY POINT

- The most commonly used metals can be bought from metal stockholders and suppliers in a range of standard shapes and sizes. Producing the metals in these forms is a very time- and energy-consuming process and it would be very expensive to make other shapes and sizes, whereas the standard ones can be bought quite cheaply.

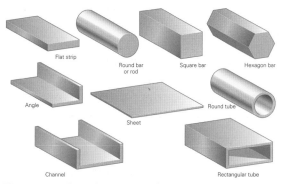

Figure 5.11 Standard metal forms

A wide range of sizes is available, but not all metals are made in the full range of sizes, so a metal supplier's stock list should be used when deciding what size is needed for a particular purpose.

Sometimes you may need to change your design slightly so that a standard size can be used. For example, if you cannot get 9 mm diameter round bar, you have to decide whether to use 8 or 10 mm instead.

Because different metals have different uses, not all are made in the full range of forms, so it is important to know what is available for each metal. The metals shown in Table 5.8 are ones that you are most likely to use or come across in your project work.

You also need to consider the cost – for example, non-ferrous metals are much more expensive than ferrous metals, so they are only used when their particular properties are needed.

Metal	Wire	Bar	Flat	Tube	Shaped sections
Mild steel		Round Square Hexagon	Strip Sheet Plate	Round Square Rectangular	Angle Channel Tee H section
Aluminium alloy	0.5–3 mm thick	Round Square Hexagon	Strip Sheet Plate	Round Square Rectangular	Angle Channel Tee
Copper	0.5–3 mm thick	Round Square	Strip Sheet	Round	
Brass	0.5–3 mm thick	Round Square Hexagon	Strip Sheet	Round	Angle

Table 5.8 Metal forms commonly available

Round and Square Bar	3, 4, 5, 6, 8, 10, 12, 16, 18, 20, 22, 25, 30, 35, 40, 45, 50 mm
Strip	10 × 3, 25 × 3, 50 × 3, 12 × 5, 20 × 5, 50 × 5, 12 × 6, 20 × 6, 50 × 6, 50 × 25, 100 × 50 mm
Sheet	1 m × 1 m, 2 m × 1 m Thickness 0.6, 0.8, 1.0, 1.2, 1.5, 2.0, 2.5, 3.0 mm
Angle	13 × 13 – 3 mm thick, 25 × 25 – 3 mm thick, 25 × 25 – 5 mm thick, 50 × 50 – 6 mm thick

Figure 5.12 Typical standard sizes for mild steel

KEY TERMS

BAR – A length of round, square, hexagonal or octagonal metal.
STRIP – Rectangular sectioned metal.
SHEET – Metal up to 3 mm thick.
TUBE – Hollow metal sections that may be round, square or rectangular.

ACTIVITY

1. Prepare a stock list of the metal bar and strip material available in your school workshop. Present the stock list as a table and give details of name of metal, type (ferrous or non-ferrous), form (round, square, strip, etc.), size and total length available.

2. Compare the amounts of ferrous and non-ferrous metals available in your school workshop. Explain why there may be more of one than the other.

▶ Plastics

KEY POINT

• Plastics are made from natural substances and most modern plastics come from coal or oil. The raw plastic material is produced as powder, granules, pellets or liquid, depending on how it will be used. In many cases, the raw material is moulded directly into shapes required for particular products, but some standard forms are also produced for more general use. Plastic products can be made self-coloured by adding colour pigments to the raw material during production.

The majority of plastics in common use are thermoplastics, which are easily moulded into shape and are also recyclable. The only thermosetting plastics you might use in project work are polyester resins for casting or glass-fibre moulding, and epoxy resin adhesives such as Araldite™. Some modern plastics are also **biodegradable**, which means that they will gradually rot away harmlessly after use.

Because plastic is easy to form, it is often cheaper to use than other materials, particularly hardwoods and some non-ferrous metals. It is possible to give plastics the appearance of other materials by the use of colour and texture, and it is sometimes difficult to tell what material something is made from.

Figure 5.13 Assortment of standard plastic forms

KEY TERM

BIODEGRADABLE – A plastic that breaks down and rots away.

ACTIVITY

Many products are now made from plastics instead of other materials. One example of this is the standard 300 mm ruler, which used to be made from wood. Give two other examples of products made from plastics that have been made from other materials in the past. Draw a labelled sketch of each product and say what advantages there are in making the product from plastic.

▶ Using the right materials

KEY POINTS

- With so many different materials to choose from, it is often difficult to decide which one to use. It is important that the material for any product is chosen carefully to ensure it is the most suitable one.

- All materials have performance characteristics that make them useful for particular applications, but this does not necessarily mean that they are the most suitable. Other factors have to be considered before it is certain that the right material has been chosen.

Example – electricity supply cables

Figure 5.14 Overhead electric power cables

Silver is the best metal for conducting electricity, so that might be thought to be the most suitable material for overhead electric power cables. However, that would simply not be possible because of the cost and the fact that there is not enough silver available. Copper is a very good conductor of electricity and is used for cables in domestic wiring, but it is too heavy to use for large overhead cables because it would sag between the pylons. That would mean that pylons would need to be closer together and many more would be needed, increasing the cost and spoiling the appearance of the landscape.

Aluminium conducts electricity quite well and is also much lighter and cheaper than copper. Overhead power cables are made from strands of aluminium wire, reinforced with steel to make them less likely to sag. This means that fewer pylons are needed to support the cables and the overall cost of the overhead power line is much lower than it would be if copper were used.

So, when we consider cost and environmental issues, aluminium is the most *suitable* metal to use for the overhead electric power cables, even though it is not the best conductor of electricity.

Example – use of manufactured boards

Figure 5.15 Boarded-up glass door

The broken glass door has been boarded up using a type of laminated board called oriented strand board (OSB), which is made from compressed flakes of wood. This board is strong and cheap but does not look good, so it has poor aesthetic properties. Because the boarding is only temporary, the appearance does not matter, and the cost and strength of the board are more important considerations. If the glass in the door were to be replaced permanently with a wooden panel, veneered plywood would be a more suitable material as it would be more aesthetically appealing as well as being strong.

Example – car manufacture

Figure 5.16 Car dashboards

The dashboards of older cars were formed in steel as part of the car's bodywork structure. This meant that they were generally quite plain because of the difficulty of producing complex shapes in the steel panels.

Modern vehicles have their dashboards formed as plastic mouldings that can be made into complex and attractive shapes. The use of plastics for dashboards also means that the shapes can be changed easily to suit new car models and design trends. Another important advantage is that less metal is used in the car body, making the vehicle lighter and more fuel efficient.

ACTIVITY

Give another example of an application where a designer could choose from any one of a number of different materials. List the materials that *could* be used and then decide which one *you* would use. You should present a good sketch of the product or application and give reasons for your choice of material.

5.4 THE CONVERSION OR ALTERING OF MATERIALS INTO OTHER USABLE FORMS

▶ Heat treatment of metals

KEY POINT

- The properties of some metals can be altered to suit particular applications by the use of heat treatment, which involves heating and cooling the metal in a carefully controlled way.

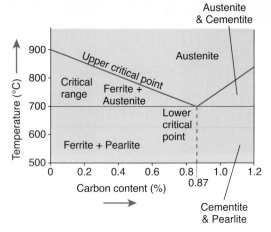

Figure 5.17 Heat treatment of steels

Heat treatment of ferrous metals

Steel is an alloy of iron and carbon, and the amount of carbon it contains governs how tough the material is and how hard it can be made by heat treatment. The structure of the grains in the steel varies according to how much carbon is in the steel and what temperature the steel is heated to. The object of heat treatment processes is to control the structure of the steel to give the properties of hardness, toughness and softness, as required.

Figure 5.17 shows the structure of steels of different carbon content and the 'critical point' temperatures at which changes take place.

Hardening and tempering

Steels with a carbon content of between 0.8 and 1.4 per cent are called high-carbon steels and these can be made hard for use as cutting tools. The process of **hardening** also makes the steel brittle, however, and some of the excess hardness is removed by **tempering** to improve the steel's toughness.

To harden a high-carbon steel, it is heated to a temperature just above the lower critical point to alter its structure. It is then left at that temperature for a short time to 'soak', which allows all of the steel to achieve the

Colour	Temp.°C	Hardness	Typical uses
Light Straw	230	Hardest	Lathe tools, scrapers
Dark Straw	245		Drills, taps and dies, punches
Orange/Brown	260		Hammer heads, plane irons
Light Purple	270		Scissors, knives
Dark Purple	280		Saws, chisels, axes
Blue	300	Toughest	Springs, spinners, vice jaws

Figure 5.18 Tempering colours and temperatures

correct temperature and structure. The steel is then **quenched** (cooled quickly) in quenching oil or brine (salt water) so that it keeps the hard structure and does not have time to change back. Because the steel is now too hard and brittle to be used, it is tempered to remove some of the hardness by heating it to a temperature of 230–300°C and then quenching again in oil or brine.

In school workshops the temperature of the steel normally has to be judged by eye, and to harden a high-carbon steel chisel it is heated to red-hot before quenching. The end of the chisel is then cleaned with emery cloth to make it clean and bright, before heating it gently until the correct tempering colour

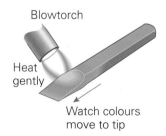
Blowtorch

Heat gently

Watch colours move to tip

Figure 5.19 Tempering a cold chisel

appears at the cutting edge. The chisel is then quenched again to leave a hard cutting edge that will be tough rather than brittle.

When hardening and tempering are carried out in industry, the steel is heated in temperature-controlled furnaces and then transferred mechanically to large quenching tanks, allowing exact control over the whole process.

Steels with less than 0.8 per cent carbon cannot be made as hard as high-carbon steels, and the medium-carbon steels, with 0.4–0.8 per cent carbon, tend to become tougher rather than harder when 'hardened' by heat treatment. Steels with less than 0.4 per cent carbon are known as mild steels and cannot be hardened in this way at all.

Case hardening

Because mild steel does not contain much carbon, it cannot be hardened in the same way as carbon steels. **Case hardening** is a process used to give mild steels a hard skin that will resist wear. The whole case-hardening process is made up of two distinct parts: **carburising**, which is the adding of carbon to the outer surface of the steel, and hardening, which makes the outer surface hard and wear-resistant.

The carburising can be done by heating the steel to red-hot and then dipping it in carbon powder so that the metal absorbs carbon. This is done two or three times before hardening the metal surface by reheating it to red-hot and quenching in water.

Another way to carburise the surface is to pack the metal in charcoal granules and **soak** it at a temperature of about 900°C for a few hours. The metal can then be removed and quenched in the normal way.

Because there is only a very thin skin of hard metal after case hardening, the centre of the steel remains tough and no tempering is needed.

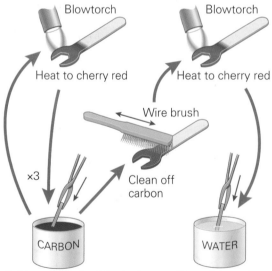

Figure 5.20 **Case hardening a mild steel spanner**

Annealing

Many metals get harder as work is done to them, which is why some become brittle and break after repeated bending or hammering.

This is called **work hardening** and the **annealing** process is used to relieve the internal stresses in metal and make it softer and easier to work. It is often used to allow metals to be bent into complex shapes more easily, or to soften the metal after work hardening has taken place

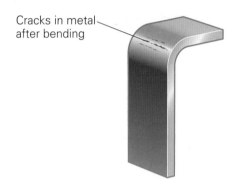

Figure 5.21 **Metal failure after work hardening**

Steel is annealed by heating it to just above the **lower critical point** and allowing it to 'soak' at that temperature for a period of time, depending on its size. The metal then needs to be allowed to cool as slowly as possible. The best way to carry out annealing is to use a temperature-controlled furnace, as the metal can be left in it to cool very slowly after it has been switched off. In the school workshop the annealing is usually done on a brazing hearth and the metal is covered with firebricks to stop it cooling too quickly.

Normalising

Normalising is carried out on steel that has become work hardened by heavy processes such as forging. Unlike annealing, the normalising process does not soften the metal, but makes it tough and ductile by refining the grain structure. Steel is normalised by heating it to just above its **upper critical point** and then allowing it to cool naturally in still air.

Annealing non-ferrous metals

The process of annealing non-ferrous metals is similar to that for steel, but it differs slightly according to the metal being annealed.

Copper is the easiest metal to anneal as it is simply heated to a dull red heat and then either quenched in water or left to cool in air.

Brass is also heated to dull red for annealing, but it must then be left to cool slowly. Brass is said to be 'hot short', which means it is brittle when red-hot and could crack if quenched in water.

When copper and brass are heated to red-hot, black scale forms on the surface of the metal. This scale can be cleaned off by putting the cooled metal in a bath of dilute sulphuric acid (pickling) or by rubbing with damp pumice powder and steel wool. If the copper is quenched in water after annealing, the black scale breaks up as the metal contracts, making it easier to clean, but this cannot be done with brass.

Aluminium is rather more difficult to anneal because of its low melting point of around 660°C; if it were to be overheated it could easily melt. To avoid overheating, the aluminium is first rubbed with soap to act as an indicator when the annealing temperature of 350–400°C is reached. The metal is then heated gently until the soap turns black and is left to cool naturally.

KEY TERMS

HARDENING – Heating and quenching steel to make it harder.

TEMPERING – Removing excess hardness and brittleness after hardening.

QUENCHING – Cooling metal down quickly in oil or salt water.

CASE HARDENING – Hardening the outer skin of mild steel.

CARBURISING – The adding of carbon to the outer surface of the steel.

WORK HARDENING – Metal getting harder by being hammered or bent.

ANNEALING – Softening metal to make it easier to work.

SOAKING – Keeping metal at a high temperature for a period of time.

LOWER AND UPPER CRITICAL POINT – the minimum and maximum points of the critical range. This is the temperature range that metal must be heated to in order to change its internal grain structure.

NORMALISING – A process carried out on steel that has become work hardened by heavy processes such as forging. It makes metal tough and ductile by refining the grain structure.

ACTIVITY

Make **two** identical cold chisels from tool steel and harden them both. Temper one of the chisels to a light straw colour and quench it. Temper the other chisel to blue before quenching it and then test the two chisels to compare them.

Test 1 – Use a chisel to cut through a piece of 3 mm mild steel held in the vice and see how much damage is done to the end of the chisel.

Test 2 – Use a file on the end of each chisel and see how much the chisel is marked by *six* strokes of the file.

Do not forget to wear goggles when carrying out these tests and keep a record of the results. Which of the two chisels do you think would be the best one to use, and why?

▶ Alloying

KEY POINT

- An alloy is a metal compound produced by combining a metal with one or more other elements, often other pure metals. Alloying is used to change the properties of the original metal and make it more useful for other applications.

Most of the alloys we come across are non-ferrous alloys that do not contain iron, but one of the most common alloys is steel, which is an alloy of iron and carbon and is therefore a ferrous alloy.

Examples of ferrous and non-ferrous alloys, their composition, working properties and uses are given in Tables 5.3 and 5.4 on pages 71–2.

▶ Composite materials

KEY POINT

- **Composite** materials are produced by combining different materials to produce better properties. Some composite materials have been around for many years and are now taken for granted, but new composites are constantly being developed as new technologies and discoveries are applied to improve materials.

There are three basic types of composite materials: particle composites, laminate composites and stranded composites.

Particle composites

Figure 5.22 Particle composite

Concrete is a good example of a **particle composite** material that has been in use for many years. It is made up of small particles of sand, cement and stone (all ceramic materials) bonded together to give a material with good strength properties. MDF and chipboard are both particle composites as they are made by bonding wood particles with resin adhesives.

More recent particle composites include materials known as **cements**, which consist of ceramic particles bonded with metal to give strong materials capable of withstanding very high temperatures. The cemented carbide tips used on saw blades, milling cutters and lathe tools are typical examples of cements.

Laminated composites

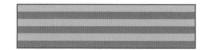

Figure 5.23 Laminated composite

The best example of a **laminated composite** material is plywood because it is very easy to see the laminates, or layers, that make up the material. It is the fact that the layers of wood are bonded together with a resin adhesive that makes plywood a composite material. Laminated glass is another good example of a laminated composite, but one that is not so easy to identify. Glass is hard and transparent, but it is not tough and breaks easily. Laminated glass consists of a thin layer of clear plastic sandwiched between two layers of glass to make the material much stronger and safer to use. **Galvanised steel** is a composite material comprised of two metals. The steel is coated with a layer of zinc to give a material that combines the corrosion resistance of zinc with the strength of steel.

Stranded composites

Figure 5.24 Stranded composite

A common form of **stranded composite** is glass-reinforced plastic (GRP) which is also known as fibreglass. Fine strands (fibres) of glass are embedded in a polyester resin to reinforce it and give the material more strength. A newer and much stronger version of this is known as carbon fibre, in which the resin is reinforced by fine strands of carbon. Although expensive, this material is very strong and also light in weight, making it well suited for use in aircraft and some car body applications.

Figure 5.25 Examples of carbon fibre and Kevlar™ products

Kevlar™ is the trade name for a very strong, lightweight polymer fibre that is well known for its use in bulletproof clothing. It is five times as strong as steel on a weight-for-weight basis and is used as the reinforcement in resin-based composites to produce lightweight structures with great strength.

KEY TERMS

COMPOSITE – A material produced by combining other different materials.
CEMENTS – Particle composites consisting of ceramic particles bonded with metal to produce strong materials.
PARTICLE COMPOSITE – Small particles of material bonded by another material.
LAMINATED COMPOSITE – Layers of materials bonded together.
GALVANISED STEEL – A composite material comprised of steel coated with a layer of zinc. It combines the corrosion resistance of zinc with the strength of steel.
STRANDED COMPOSITE – Strands or fibres bonded in another material.

ACTIVITY

Use the internet to research further examples of composite materials and their uses. Keep a copy of the information about these new materials in your notes.

5.5 SMART AND MODERN MATERIALS

'Smart' materials react to external changes such as temperature or light and appear to react intelligently. For example, the test strip on drink cans will turn blue when the drink is chilled to the right temperature.

▶ Shape memory alloy

An example of **shape memory alloy** (SMA) is nitinol, a mixture of nickel and titanium. Although available in many different shapes, its most common use is as wire. SMA works by remembering a shape when heated to a specific temperature. At room temperature the wire can be bent and it will retain this shape, but when heated to the original temperature, the 'transition' temperature, it will return to its original shape. This process can be repeated thousands of times.

SMA wire can be used to move parts of robots and to open or close valves or bolts. Three applications of smart wire are shown in Figures 5.26–5.28, providing movement in a straight line, rotary movement and activating a lever on a model of a barrier.

Door bolt

SMA wire used in an electric door lock

Compression spring keeps SMA wire stretched and bolt in 'locked' position

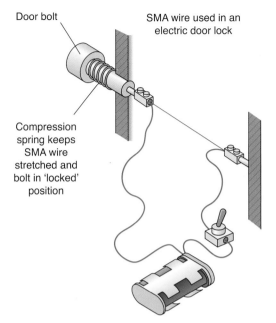

Figure 5.26 SMA wire used in an electric door lock

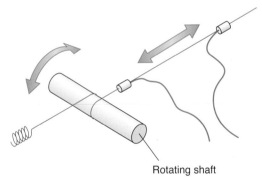

Rotating shaft

Figure 5.27 SMA wire coiled around a drum, shaft or pulley, producing rotary movement

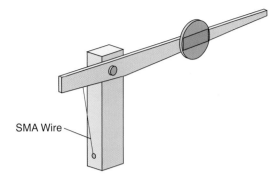

SMA Wire

Figure 5.28 SMA wire used to activate a lever on a model barrier

⟩ Shape memory polymers

Many plastics have a 'memory' and these are known as **shape memory polymers**. The most common that you are likely to have worked with is acrylic. When heated, the plastic becomes pliable and can be shaped. After it has been allowed to cool it can be reheated and it returns to its original shape.

Four stages involved in making an acrylic key fob are shown below.

Stage 1

Heat the acrylic in an oven to soften it. Press the letters 'KEYS' into the surface of the acrylic using a weight or scrap wood and G cramp.

Stage 2

The letters will have made an indentation in the acrylic. Allow the acrylic to cool.

Figure 5.29

Stage 3

File or sand down the acrylic so that the letters 'KEYS' are just visible.

Stage 4

Reheat the acrylic and the letters 'KEYS' will now stand out above the surface of the acrylic. The plastic has remembered its shape.

▶ Polymorph

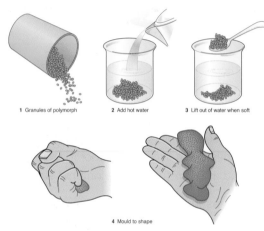

1 Granules of polymorph   2 Add hot water   3 Lift out of water when soft

4 Mould to shape

Figure 5.30 Four stages using polymorph

Polymorph is a thermoplastic supplied in granular form. It is a 'smart' polymer because the granules become soft when immersed in hot water and the plastic can then be moulded by hand to the required shape. By re-immersing the plastic in hot water it can be remoulded. At room temperature polymorph can be machined and cut in the same way as other plastics. Polymorph is excellent for handles of tools as it can be ergonomically shaped, and since it shrinks as it cools there is no need to glue it onto the tool itself.

▶ Thermochromic materials

Thermochromic materials change colour at specific temperatures. The material is incorporated into a special ink and then printed onto plastic to produce thermometers or temperature indicators. One popular application is the test strip on the side of a battery. The strip is pressed at each end, and if the battery is in good condition, current flows through a printed resistor under a thermochromic film and heats it, producing a colour change.

Figure 5.31 Test strip on a battery

Thermochromic sheet

This material is a black plastic (self-adhesive) film, coated with thermochromic ink. When heated from its original temperature, the sheet turns bright blue, showing clearly that there has been a change in temperature. The sheet can be cut into any shape and added to products, such as electronic circuitry and food containers, to show when the temperature is too high.

Thermochromic pigments

Thermochromic pigments are supplied in paste form and can be mixed with any type of acrylic paint. When applied to coffee mugs, for example, the colour is visible (Figure 5.32), but as the hot water is poured into the mug the colour disappears and an image can be seen (Figures 5.33–5.35). When

Figure 5.32

Figure 5.33

Figure 5.34

Figure 5.35

the temperature falls, the colour returns. It is possible to mix the pigment with acrylic paints of different colours. Other applications for these pigments include kitchenware, baby feeding spoons and drink stirrers.

Photochromic materials

Photochromic materials change colour according to the light available. One popular application is spectacles that react to changing light conditions by darkening in bright sunlight. The pigment can be used in exactly the same way as for thermochromic pigment.

ACTIVITY

Think of as many products as you can associated with heat in one form or another and consider how thermochromic materials could be used in their design.

▌ Modern wood-based and metal-based materials

Many of the developments with traditional materials such as wood and metal do not appear as exciting as the visual impression made by 'smart' materials, but they are very important. Some of the materials described

will have practical applications for your projects in design and technology, while some will have more commercial or industrial uses.

Flexiply®

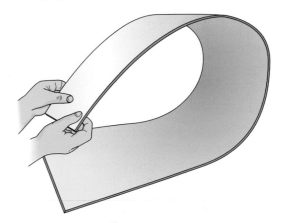

Figure 5.36 Flexiply®

You will already know about plywood and how it is used, but Flexiply® has numerous advantages over traditional plywood. The name tells you about its additional property – the ability to be bent to shape by hand to radii as small as 25 mm. Sheets are available as 2440 x 1220 mm and thicknesses of 3 mm, 5 mm, 8 mm and 15 mm. No special equipment is needed to bend it, and complex multi-radii shapes can be produced.

ACTIVITY

Think of products that are made from metal or plastic because of their ability to be bent to shape. Which of these could be replaced with Flexiply®?

Flexi-veneer

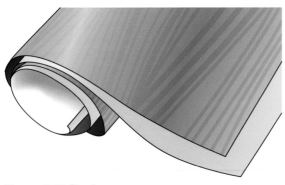

Figure 5.37 Flexi-veneer

If you have ever picked up a sheet of veneer you will know how brittle or delicate it can be and how easily it can split. Flexi-veneer helps to overcome this problem. Flexi-veneer is a paper-backed product 0.8 mm thick, supplied as a roll. Flexi-veneer can be cut using a knife or even a laser cutter.

Hexaboard

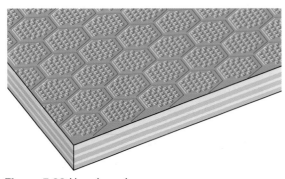

Figure 5.38 Hexaboard

Hexaboard is mainly used by industry because of its extreme durability. Hexaboard is a PVC-laminated plywood. Applications include flooring for some commercial aircraft and as tea chests.

Anodised aluminium sheet

Anodising is a process similar to electroplating. It involves thickening the thin film of oxide on the surface of the aluminium sheet, using coloured dyes to create an attractive metallic finish. Aluminium can only be anodised on a small scale in a school workshop, so it is useful to know that there is a form of aluminium sheet pre-anodised, ready for use, available in a range of colours and thicknesses. The sheet can be worked using traditional metalworking tools such as saws, drills and punches.

Aluminium composite sheet

This sheet is a composite because it has a polythene core sandwiched between aluminium backing sheets. The backing sheets are available in different colours. It is lightweight, rigid, weather and corrosion resistant, retains a high level of flatness, has good thermal insulation and impact resistance. Because of these properties it is used for panelling and fascias on buildings.

▶ Nanotechnology

Nanotechnology is the science of the 'very small'. It is concerned with the control of 'matter' on an atomic and molecular scale. To give you some idea of how small a scale we are talking about, one nanometre is equal to one-millionth of a millimetre.

One example of this technology is carbon. When carbon atoms are arranged in one way, diamonds are produced; arrange them another way and we have graphite for pencils; arrange them randomly and we produce soot.

One exciting development in nanotechnology is the production of carbon nanotubes: with the right arrangement of atoms it is possible to produce a material that is hundreds of times stronger than steel, yet much lighter.

Some of the applications of nanotechnology include tennis racquets, golf clubs and cycle frames, and as coatings for products such as self-cleaning glass and water-repellent wood.

KEY POINT

- Be aware of other 'smart' and modern materials as they become available. Material science has developed rapidly over the last 30 years and it is impossible to keep pace with all the developments in this field. By the time you are reading this information there are likely to be many more new materials incorporated into the design of everyday products. As an ongoing part of your studies you should keep an open and inquiring mind regarding new materials and try to research the latest articles, whether you have come across them on the television news or on recommended internet websites.

KEY TERMS

'SMART' MATERIALS – Materials that appear to react intelligently to external changes such as temperature or light.

SHAPE MEMORY ALLOY – Known as nitinol, it works by remembering a shape when heated to a specific temperature. At room temperature it can be bent and will retain this shape, but will return to its original shape when heated to the original temperature.

SHAPE MEMORY POLYMERS – When heated, this type of plastic is pliable and can be shaped but once it has cooled it can be reheated and returned to its original shape. Acrylic is an example of a shape memory polymer.

POLYMORPH – A thermoplastic that is a 'smart' polymer because when immersed in hot water it can be moulded by hand to the required shape. By re-immersing the plastic in hot water it can be remoulded. At room temperature it can be machined and cut and it shrinks as it cools.

THERMOCHROMIC MATERIALS – These change colour at specific temperatures. The material is incorporated into a special ink and then printed onto plastic to produce thermometers or temperature indicators.

PHOTOCHROMIC MATERIALS – These change colour according to the light available.

NANOTECHNOLOGY – The science concerned with the control of 'matter' on an atomic and molecular scale. One nanometre is equal to one-millionth of a millimetre.

5.6 PRE-MANUFACTURED STANDARD COMPONENTS

There will be occasions in your school workshop when you will construct and assemble a product, perhaps a wall cabinet, toolbox or coffee table, and need to use a woodscrew, hinge, handle, bracket or knock-down fitting. These are all examples of pre-manufactured standard components. Your design and technology department will stock some essential items, but you may need to visit your local DIY store to buy some of these yourself. This section will look at a whole range of components used in the design and manufacture of everyday products. Because there are thousands of different components, this section includes examples that could be important to both your coursework project and to prepare you for possible examination questions.

Woodscrews

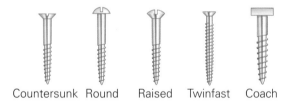

Countersunk Round   Raised   Twinfast   Coach

Figure 5.39 Common types of woodscrew

Countersunk head

A countersunk head is used when you want the head of the screw to be level with or slightly below the surface, for example when fitting hinges.

Round head

A round head is used to fasten thin sheet materials such as metal or plastic to wood. The area under the head is able to spread the pressure applied.

Raised head

A raised head is used for decorative purposes, for example, when fitting door furniture such as handles and door plates.

Twinfast

A twinfast is used specifically on chipboard because the coarse thread provides greater holding power.

Coach

A coach is used where great holding power is required; for example, the metalwork vices in your workshop will be fastened to the benches using coach screws. They are tightened with a spanner.

What materials are woodscrews made from?

Woodscrews are made mainly of steel or brass. Since steel screws can rust, some are galvanised (zinc-coated) for outdoor use.

Some are chrome-plated for decorative purposes. Brass screws are softer than steel, so care must be taken when screwing these into hardwoods to avoid them snapping. Some steel screws are painted black, known as 'black-japanned', and are suitable for outdoor use.

Straight slot   Phillips   Pozidriv

Figure 5.40 Types of screwdriver slots

The main advantage of using Phillips® or Pozidriv® slot screws is that the tip of the screwdriver is less likely to slip out and damage the head of the screw or the surface of the wood.

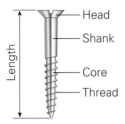

Figure 5.41 Parts of a woodscrew

When choosing woodscrews you will need to answer the following questions:

- How many? (Carpenters and joiners may buy screws in boxes of 200, but smaller packs are available from DIY stores.)
- What type of head? (Phillips®, Pozidriv® or straight)
- What material? (Steel, brass, galvanised or black-japanned)
- What length?

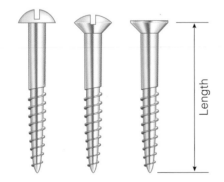

Figure 5.42 Measuring the length of a woodscrew

- What gauge? (Gauge is the 'thickness' of the woodscrew and is referred to with a number. For example, gauge number 4 is approximately Ø3 mm, 6 is Ø3.5 mm, 8 is Ø4.5 mm and 10 is Ø5 mm. These gauges are the most commonly used and you will notice that they are all even numbers.)

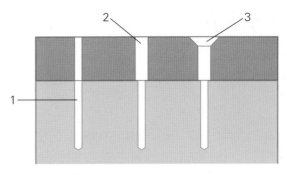

Figure 5.43 Preparing two pieces of wood to be screwed together with countersunk screws

When preparing to screw together two pieces of wood with countersunk screws, you should take the following steps, as shown in Figure 5.43.

1. Drill a pilot hole to the diameter of the core.
2. Drill a clearance hole slightly larger than the diameter of the shank.
3. Drill the countersunk for the head to 'sit' in.

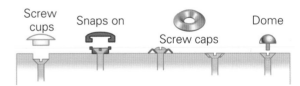

Figure 5.44 Caps and cups

There are various types of caps and cups available to push onto, screw into or position under screw heads to improve their appearance. The dome is a particularly good screw-in cap used to screw a mirror to a wall.

Nails

Using nails is the quickest way to join pieces of wood. To work, they depend on the friction between the sides of the nail and the wood. There are serrations around the shank of a

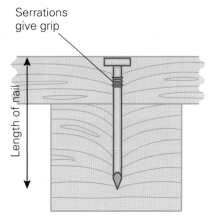

Figure 5.45 Two pieces of wood fastened with a nail

nail that provide extra grip. When buying nails you will need to know the type of nail for the job, the length and the material. Most nails are made from steel, but there are galvanised types as well as brass and copper.

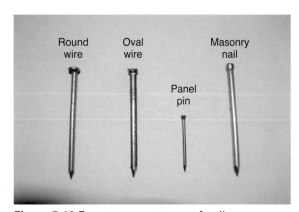

Figure 5.46 Four common types of nail

Round wire nails

These are used for general joinery work and range in length from 12 to 150 mm.

Oval wire nails

These are used for interior joinery. Because they have virtually no head, they can be hidden easily and filled. It is important that they are driven into the wood along the grain,

otherwise their oval shape could split the wood. They range in length from 12 to 150 mm.

Panel pins

These are used with small-scale work and pinning thin sheet material. They range in length from 12 to 50 mm.

Masonry nails

These are particularly useful if you want to fasten into brickwork or mortar.

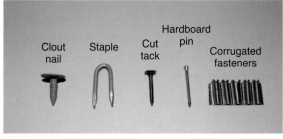

Figure 5.47 Five common types of fastening

Clout nails

These are used specifically to fasten roofing felt to shed roofs. They are galvanised to prevent rusting. They have a wide head to prevent the felt from splitting and give extra-wide pressure.

Staples

These are used to make packing crates and in upholstery work. Square types of staple are fired from a gun, whereas the round staple would be hammered into the wood.

Cut tacks

These are used in upholstery to fasten fabric to wooden frames. Because of their appearance they are usually hidden in use.

Hardboard pins

These are used to fasten hardboard to frames. Because of their pointed head they do not need to be punched below the surface of the wood.

Corrugated fasteners

Corrugated fasteners are used to make quick, cheap corner joints in wooden frames. They are hammered in across each corner.

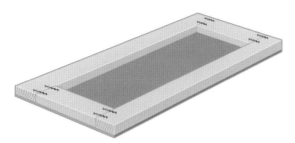

Figure 5.48 Frame shown with corrugated fasteners in each corner

Nailing techniques

When you nail a frame together, you should stagger the positions of the nails to avoid splitting the wood along the grain.

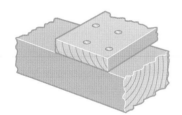

Figure 5.49 Staggered nailing

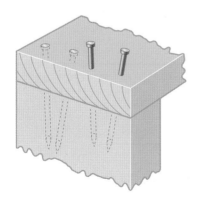

Figure 5.50 Dovetail nailing

Hammering nails into the wood at a slight angle, or 'dovetailed', will make the joint stronger and more difficult to pull apart.

▶ Nuts, bolts and machine screws

These are used to make temporary joints because they can be taken apart using a screwdriver, spanner or Allen key.

Bolts

Bolts are made from high-tensile steel and have either square or hexagonal heads. They are ordered by the diameter of the thread and their length is measured from underneath the head of the bolt. Some bolts have the thread along their whole length. You can exert great force when tightening bolts with a spanner.

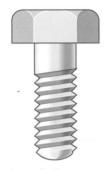

Figure 5.51 Drawing of a hexagonal head bolt

Nuts

Wing nut Hexagonal nut Square nut Locking nut Castle nut and split pin Nylon (fibre lock) nut

Figure 5.52 Six types of nut

Nuts have the same types of head as bolts, but wing nuts are specially shaped to be finger-tightened. Lock nuts are designed to prevent loosening of the joint caused by vibration. The castle nut is used in those situations where there must be no risk of the nut coming off as a result of vibration. They are used on cars to tighten wheel bearings.

Machine screws

Machine screws are available in a variety of lengths, diameters and types of head. Most can be tightened using a screwdriver, but socket-head machine screws need an Allen key. Allen keys give a very positive fit when tightening the screw, and considerable force can be applied without the danger of the tool slipping out.

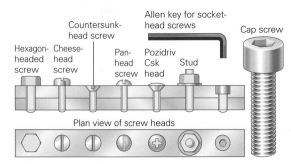

Figure 5.53 Seven types of machine screw

Self-tapping screws

Self-tapping screws are made from hardened steel and they cut their own thread as they are screwed into thin sheet material such as metal or plastic. Common sizes are 6 to 50 mm. They can have straight, Phillips® or Posidriv® slots.

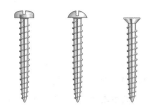

Figure 5.54 Three types of self-tapping screw

Washers

The purpose of a washer is to protect the surface on which the bolt or nut is being tightened, to spread the load and prevent the fixing from vibrating loose.

Plain washer · Lock washer · Grover spring washer · Spring washer · Tab washer · Serrated washer

Figure 5.55 Six types of washer

Knock-down fittings

Knock-down (KD) fittings are used in the construction of furniture. Be careful not to assume flat-pack designed furniture only has KD fittings. While many items of flat-pack do use KD fittings, they also use permanent joints for self-assembly, such as dowel, and supply glue for the consumer to assemble the item. Many of the KD fittings include the use of dowel or metal pins to locate part of the joint. Most of the KD fittings can be fitted using basic tools such as a drill, hammer, mallet and screwdriver. This is a definite advantage for the consumer. There is a wide variety of KD fittings used in the manufacture of furniture, some of which are available at DIY stores.

One-piece and two-piece corner blocks

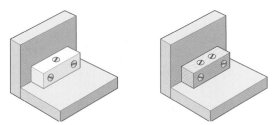

Figure 5.56 One-piece plastic corner block and one-piece wooden corner block

One-piece corner blocks made from plastic are used to join the sides of a cabinet. You could make your own from wood. Remember to use countersunk screws.

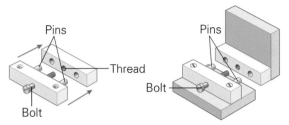

Figure 5.57 Two-piece plastic corner block

A single-threaded bolt fastens one part to the other, while two pins help to locate the two parts. The left-hand part is screwed to the inside of the cabinet.

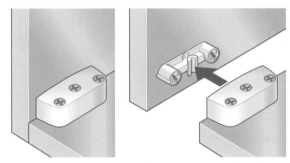

Figure 5.58 A variation of the two-piece plastic corner block

Figure 5.58 shows another type of two-piece fitting. Both parts are screwed against the inside of the cabinet and a final screw is inserted on top of the fitting to keep it in place.

Rigid joint

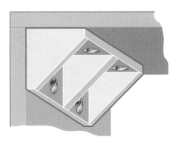

Figure 5.59 Rigid joint

A rigid joint is made from a single piece of moulded plastic and four screws are used to hold the joint in place.

Scan fittings

Scan fittings can be used to join frames or the sides of cabinets together. A hole is drilled through the leg into the end of the rail. The aluminium barrel is dropped into a hole drilled into the top of the rail. The aluminum barrel has a threaded hole for the Allen screw to screw into and pull the joint together. A metal locating pin helps to align the two parts.

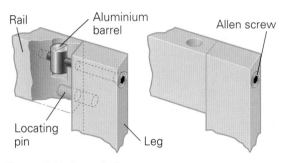

Figure 5.60 Scan fitting

Cam lock

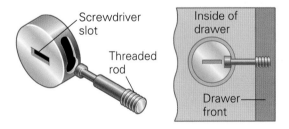

Figure 5.61 Cam lock

One very common use for cam locks is to fasten a drawer front to the sides of the drawer. A threaded rod is screwed into the inside of the drawer front. The circular cam lock is dropped into a drilled hole in the drawer side. A screwdriver is used to turn the cam lock, which then pulls the drawer front towards it, tightening the joint. This is a particularly clever mechanical joint using the principle of the cam.

Leg fastenings

It can be particularly useful to be able to take the legs apart from the rest of a table for storage purposes. While the shapes of the two connecting steel plates are different, the principle is the same. A rod has a woodscrew thread on one end to fit into the leg of the table. On the other end is a screw thread onto which a nut can be tightened.

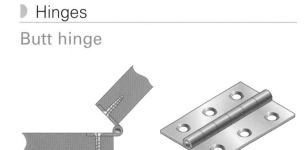

Figure 5.62 Two variations of a leg fastening

▌ Hinges

Butt hinge

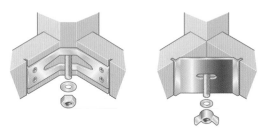

Figure 5.63 Butt hinge

Butt hinges are one of the most commonly used hinges. They are used for doors, windows and large and small boxes. They are usually recessed into the edge of the wood so that they look very neat. They are commonly made from steel or brass. Fitting a hinge into the edge of a small jewellery box

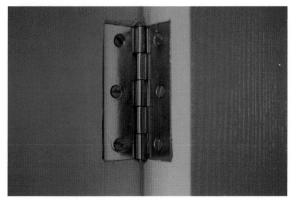

Figure 5.64

or cabinet takes a lot of care and skill to achieve a high level of appearance.

Back-flap hinge

Figure 5.65 Back-flap hinge

Back-flap hinges are used for flaps or 'leaves' on tables or for large lids on boxes. The greater surface area and the spaced holes provide greater strength. In addition, the positions of the holes make them less likely to split the grain, which can happen with butt hinges where the screw holes are all in line.

Piano hinge

Figure 5.66 Piano hinge

The name gives a clue to their use. Piano hinges are used where you need a lot of support along the edges of a long product. A case for a snooker cue might use a piano hinge.

Tee hinge

Tee hinges are used on gates and sheds. The long arm with staggered holes would be fastened to the door and give it great support. They are black-japanned (galvanised) to prevent rusting.

Figure 5.67 Tee hinge

Figure 5.68

Flush hinge

Flush hinges are popular with students because they require no recessing. They are surface-mounted and one flap fits inside the other when closed.

Figure 5.69 Flush hinge

Adjustable concealed hinge

Manufacturers of kitchen cabinets often use adjustable concealed hinges. These hinges give consumers the opportunity to adjust a cabinet door up and down and in and out, simply by loosening and/or tightening particular screws in the hinge itself.

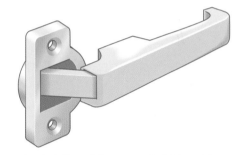

Figure 5.70 Adjustable concealed hinge

Figure 5.71

Stays

Stays are a type of hinge in as much as they connect two parts of a cabinet, for example, and allow the 'fall' on the cabinet to open and close. Good-quality stays are made from solid drawn brass. There are lots of different types

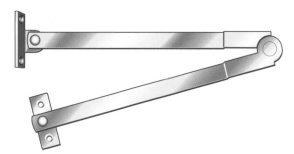

Figure 5.72 Brass stay

Figure 5.73 Brass stay with adjustment

of stay, but they all have to screw against the inside of the cabinet and to the 'fall'. The stay in Figure 5.73 has adjustable resistance, that is, it can be made to fall (open) with little force or needing increased force.

▶ Catches

There are three main types of catch used to keep closed lids on boxes or doors on cabinets: ball, spring and magnetic. They are available in a variety of materials, including brass and plastic, depending on the type of product to which they will be fitted.

Ball catch

Ball catches are neat and can be recessed so that they are hardly noticeable. They are available in very small sizes for small-scale cabinet work, or a much larger ball catch can be used to close a door positively.

Figure 5.74 Ball catch

Spring catch

Spring catches give a very positive fastening, but tend to be less attractive in appearance and therefore are used for more functional products.

Figure 5.75 Spring catch

Magnetic catch

Figure 5.76 Magnetic catch

These are available in a variety of materials. Some are made from brass when used on quality cabinet work, while others are made from white plastic and are more suitable for kitchen cabinets.

▶ Drawer and door runners

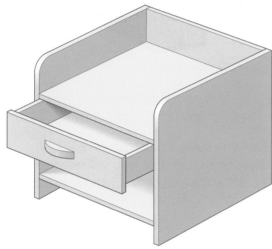

Figure 5.77 Bedside cabinet made from veneered chipboard and sold as flat-pack for self-assembly

This bedside cabinet could be designed and made by a student for their coursework project. The drawer will 'run' inside the

cabinet. There are several ways of supporting the drawer. You could put a shelf inside, but this would use more materials and increase the weight and cost.

One good way of supporting the drawer is to produce a groove in the side of the drawer and add a strip to the inside of cabinet. The strip could be pinned and glued in position.

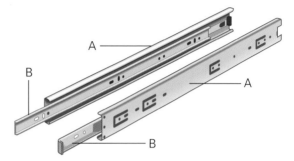

Figure 5.79 Drawer runners

Another way is to buy a pair of drawer runners, as shown in Figure 5.79. Parts A are screwed to the inside of the cabinet, while parts B are screwed to the outside of the drawer. They operate by parts B sliding in and out of A. There are different lengths and

Figure 5.78 Drawer inside cabinet

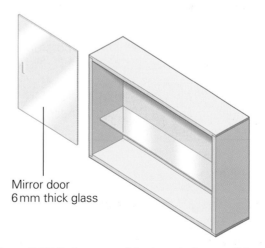

Mirror door
6 mm thick glass

Figure 5.80 Bathroom cabinet made from solid wood with two glass sliding doors and adjustable shelf

types of runners and some would be screwed underneath the drawer.

With glass sliding doors, the cabinet must be assembled first and then the doors fitted. You must make sure that the doors can be removed for cleaning or replacement if they break. There are three ways of doing this, as described below.

Figure 5.82 Plastic runners

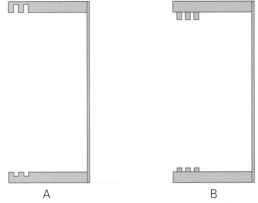

A   B

Figure 5.81 Methods of producing 'runners'

In cabinet A you could cut two grooves in the bottom and two grooves in the top of the cabinet. In cabinet B you could add three strips to the top and bottom to make the grooves. Remember, the grooves in the top must be twice as deep as the grooves in the bottom, so that you can lift the doors up into the groove.

The third way is to buy lengths of plastic 'channelling' from a DIY store. These can be glued in position.

▶ Drawer and cabinet handles

When you make a cabinet with either a drawer or a small door, you will need some type of handle or 'pull' so that you can open and close it easily. Many students enjoy making their own handles to match their product, but there are hundreds of different types available, either at DIY stores or through mail-order hardware catalogues. There is a vast range of materials, finishes and styles. The advantage of buying a special handle is that it can give your work a really professional finish.

Beech   Polished brass   Anodised aluminium   Oak   Chromed finish

Figure 5.83 Drawer/cabinet handles

▶ Locks

There are many different locks available for a wide range of purposes. Some of these are technically 'catches', used to fasten rather than lock. You will have seen these used on doors, drawers, toolboxes and wooden cases.

Hasp and staple

This would be used with a padlock to fasten a shed door or gate for security.

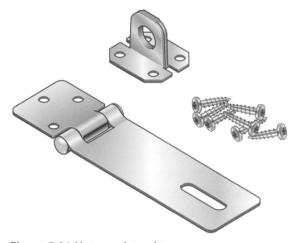

Figure 5.84 Hasp and staple

Toggle catch

Although these cannot be locked, they can be used to fasten the top and bottom parts of a toolbox or similar case together.

Figure 5.85 Toggle catch

Box-style cupboard catch

There are many variations of this type of catch used on cabinets and cupboards.

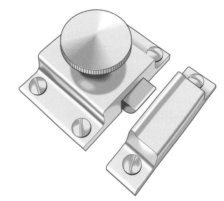

Figure 5.86 Box-style cupboard catch

ACTIVITY

1. Look at the cabinet shown in Figure 5.87.

Name and sketch a pre-manufactured component that could be used in the following situations:

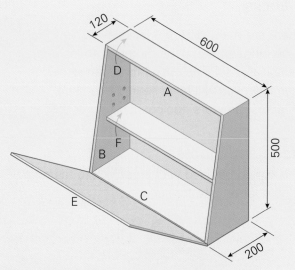

Figure 5.87 Cabinet requiring six different pre-manufactured components

A To hold the door closed against the cabinet.

B To provide a moving joint between the door and the inside of the cabinet so that the door can remain horizontal when open.

C To provide a moving joint between the door and the cabinet.

D A KD fitting to join the sides of the cabinet.

E A component that allows you to open or close the door.

F A component that supports the adjustable shelf.

2. Read the information about knock-down fittings, hinges, catches and so on. Look at the furniture you have at home and see how many of the pre-manufactured components we have discussed in this section are used in their manufacture.

CHAPTER 6

TOOLS AND EQUIPMENT FOR MAKING PRODUCTS

By the end of this chapter you should have developed a knowledge and understanding of:

- the importance of health and safety when designing and making products in school workshops
- risk assessment
- tools – their selection and effective and safe use
- alternative tools and equipment that can be used for the same task
- safety checks to be carried out on electrical equipment before use.

This chapter deals with a wide range of tools and equipment that you will need to know about when making products from resistant materials. You will need to be able to identify specific tools or equipment for a particular purpose. Your teacher will show you how to use them properly and safely. Written examinations include questions about these tools and equipment and their correct use.

6.1 HEALTH AND SAFETY

When products are designed and manufactured it is important that they are safe to make and safe to use.

Health and safety is concerned with the well-being of everyone involved with the products during their manufacture and with consumers who purchase the products and use them.

- Products must be able to withstand misuse. For example, a child's toy that falls apart when it is accidentally dropped could

be dangerous to the child. Therefore it is important to consider the choice of materials, construction or manufacturing processes and the finish that is applied to the toy.

- Products must conform to safety standards in all countries where they are to be sold, for example the lion mark on a child's toy sold in Europe.

- Where necessary, products should include

detailed instructions on use. When using an electric lawnmower or a food processor, for example, it would be essential to have detailed instructions.

- Where maintenance of a product may be carried out by consumers, it must be safe to do so, for example when replacing the blade on an electric lawnmower or cleaning the blades on a food processor.

- Some products may need specific labelling about possible dangers, for example a lamp giving the safe maximum wattage of a light bulb to be used.

You also need to consider the working environment in which the products are manufactured and the conditions under which the workforce operates.

- The workplace must be well organised so that specific tasks may be carried out safely; for example, a heat treatment area such as a welding bay must be kept separate from other production areas.

- Walkways or gangways should be clearly marked and there should be specific areas where consumable goods or tools are stored out of the way to avoid obstacles.

- Chemicals, solvents, flammable and toxic substances must be stored and handled with extreme care. Employers are required by law to carry out 'risk assessments' of these substances. (Risk assessment is dealt with later in this chapter.)

- There should be adequate space at workstations so that the machine operators can work safely.

- Lighting should be adequate so that tasks can be carried out safely.

- The temperature in which employees work should be comfortable, taking into account the type of processes being undertaken.

- Where machinery is used, it is essential that:
  - instructions for use are clearly displayed near to the machine
  - warning hazards and regulations relating to safety clothing or eye protection are clearly displayed
  - companies provide adequate training in the use of machinery
  - emergency 'stop' buttons are provided
  - regular maintenance is carried out to ensure that tools are safe
  - faulty machinery should be clearly labelled and taken out of use.

- Procedures for emergency evacuation in the event of a fire and the reporting of accidents should be clearly displayed.

6.2 PERSONAL SAFETY

Personal protective wear

When carrying out practical work you need to consider what protective wear you need to use in order to carry out the activity safely.

- Goggles provide eye protection when using the drilling machine, lathes, sanding disk or certain types of machine saw.

- Face masks or respirators should be used when spray painting and during any operation that creates dust, such as sanding, or toxic fumes.

- Visors give full face protection, for example when casting hot metal.
- Aprons give general protection to clothing, while leather aprons are essential when casting hot metals.
- Leggings should be worn when casting hot metals.
- Steel-capped shoes should be worn where any heavy work is undertaken.
- Ear defenders should be used when drilling or cutting with heavy machinery.
- Rubber/plastic disposable gloves should be worn when using chemicals.

Some chemicals, such as catalysts and resins used in glass-fibre work, can harm the skin and may cause irritation, or even a skin disease called dermatitis. To minimise this risk, gloves should be worn. In addition, barrier cream rubbed into the hands and arms will provide a high level of protection. After use, the cream should be washed off with soap and water.

Machine guards

Figure 6.1 Lathe guards

Machine guards are designed to protect you from a variety of dangers by enclosing the tool behind impact-resistant clear plastic shielding. Some guards, such as those around a drilling machine, are designed to adjust up and down as the drill bit is brought down onto the workpiece.

With some machines the danger may be the sharpness of the cutting tool or an abrasive surface that can cause injury.

With many machines the danger is the moving parts which could cause you or your clothing to become entangled in the machine.

Some of the machines you may be familiar with – such as drills, lathes and milling machines – must, by law, have adequate guards.

Dust and fume extraction

Figure 6.2 Dust extraction unit

Precautions must be taken when carrying out processes that create dust, for example using a sanding disk. Tiny particles of dust can be breathed in or enter your eyes.

Processes that create toxic fumes, such as spray painting or working with glass-reinforced plastic resins, also require great care.

Dust and fume extraction units are very effective when they are fitted closely and directly to the machine or equipment.

Disposal of waste

Within most manufacturing environments there is likely to be waste. It is important that waste materials are not allowed to build up and that they are disposed of properly. Much waste from wood, metal and plastic is relatively harmless, but chemicals need to be disposed of by specialist companies that collect them from the manufacturer's premises.

Accident procedures

In the workshop it is essential that you know what to do in the event of an accident.

- Do not panic.
- Always tell your teacher immediately, no matter how minor you may consider the accident to be.
- Make sure you know where the first aid box is.
- Make sure you know where the emergency stop buttons are in the workshop.

6.3 RISK ASSESSMENT

Risk assessment is the process, required by law, to be undertaken by companies, including schools, to identify potentially dangerous situations in their workplace and to explain how the risks may be reduced or eliminated, so that everyone connected with the company or school can operate in a safe and healthy environment.

There are five stages in carrying out a risk assessment:

1. Identify the process, operation or substance.
2. Identify the possible hazard.
3. Consider the risk – that is, how likely it is that the hazard will occur.
4. Explain the control measures you need to carry out to provide protection.
5. Explain what emergency measures you need to carry out in the event of personal injury.

6.4 COSHH

COSHH stands for the Control of Substances Hazardous to Health. It is the way that employers assess the risks from using substances that could be very dangerous to our health; it is one part of risk assessment.

Instructions relating to potentially hazardous substances

There are many potentially dangerous substances used in school workshops, including Tensol cement, superglue, impact adhesives and some paints. Your teachers will have carried out risk assessments for each of these substances.

Look at the following risk assessment for students and teachers using Tensol cement.

Process or operation	Hazards	Risk assessment	Control measures
Spreading cement onto surfaces of acrylic plastic to be joined together	May enter through the skin and by swallowing	There would have to be a huge spillage in the workshop or it would have to be used in a very confined space to pose a real hazard	Use in well-ventilated areas
	Irritant to the skin, eyes and lungs	Splashes from the cement would need to be kept off the skin and away from eyes	Apply barrier cream and/or wear protective gloves; eye protection must be worn
	Highly flammable	Vapour from Tensol could be ignited by flames or red-hot metal	Work must be kept at least 1 m away from flames or red-hot metal

Table 6.1 Risk assessment for Tensol cement

6.5 SAFETY SYMBOLS USED IN THE WORKSHOP

Wash your hands

Wear eye protection

Wear ear protection

HIGHLY FLAMMABLE

Corrosive

Toxic

Chemicals

Figure 6.3 Safety signs

There will be a number of signs used in your workshop areas. You need to know what they mean and what you need to do to comply with them.

- Blue signs are mandatory – that is, you **must** do what they say.
- Black and yellow signs are warnings.
- Red diamonds are warnings of hazards.

ACTIVITY

1. Make a room plan of one of your school workshops. Draw the positions of the workbenches, tables, cupboards, machines and emergency stop buttons. Make a list of all the 'good' or safe features and a list of all the 'poor' or potentially unsafe features.

2. Carry out two risk assessments when using:
   - a drilling machine
   - polyurethane varnish.

3. Look carefully at the student using the drilling machine in Figure 6.4. Identify five safe working practices.

Figure 6.4

KEY TERMS

RISK ASSESSMENT – A process required by law that is undertaken by companies, including schools, to identify potentially dangerous situations in their workplace and to explain how the risks may be reduced or eliminated.

COSHH – Control of Substances Hazardous to Health. It is concerned with how employers assess the risks from using substances that could be dangerous to health and is part of the risk assessment process.

6.6 SAFETY CHECKS ON ELECTRICAL EQUIPMENT

Always be aware of the potential dangers in your workshop. For example, portable electrical equipment needs to be robust and well maintained due to the nature of its use. Always check the equipment visually for obvious dangers, such as a frayed or damaged cable on electrical soldering irons or drills. Make sure that there are no loose screws on plugs. If you are in any doubt, do not use the equipment and inform your teacher of your concerns.

6.7 CHECKING MACHINE SETTINGS

There are a number of settings and checks that are common to drilling machines and centre lathes, which should be carried out every time the machine is used. Always make sure that:

- the workpiece is held securely in a chuck or vice

- the correct drill, lathe tool or milling cutter is selected and that it is in good condition

- the drill, lathe tool or milling cutter is held securely in the chuck, arbor or spindle

- the correct speed is set in terms of the size of the drill, tool or cutter used and the material to be cut

- chuck keys are removed before switching on

- guards are in place and eye protection is worn.

6.8 PROCESSES USED IN THE MAKING OF PRODUCTS

▶ Preparing, marking out, measuring and testing

The tools and equipment discussed in this section are designed to be used specifically with wood, metal or plastics. However, some can be used with wood and metal, or metal and plastic, or wood and plastic. It is important to be able to identify the correct tool or equipment for the material that you are working with.

Datum faces

Datum faces are sides, edges or ends of material that are perfectly flat and are used to measure or mark out from. Without a flat surface to work from, all your measurements will be inaccurate.

Steel rule

This is used to measure and also to test for flatness.

Marking knife

This is used to mark lines across the grain of wood. The knife cuts the fibres of the wood; it is thinner than a pencil mark and can act as a guide when sawing.

Scriber

The scriber is used to mark out lines on metal or on plastic. It is important that the lines marked on plastic are sawn down or hidden as they cannot be removed.

Chinagraph pencil

This is used to mark out on plastic as it can be rubbed out easily if a mistake is made. Sometimes a non-permanent felt-tip marker is just as good.

Try square

The try square can be used on wood, metal and plastic to mark a line at 90 degrees to an edge. It can also be used to test how square an edge is. Woodworkers' try squares have a wooden stock and a carbon steel blade, while engineers' squares are made entirely from carbon steel.

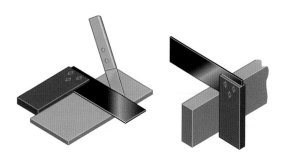

Figure 6.5 Try square

Marking gauge

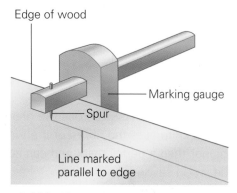

Figure 6.6 Marking gauge

This is used on wood to draw a line along the grain, parallel to an edge.

Cutting gauge

This is used on wood to draw a line across the grain, parallel to an end. The difference between a marking gauge and a cutting gauge is that the marking gauge has a spur that makes the mark, while the cutting gauge has a small blade to cut across the fibres of the wood.'

Mortise gauge

The mortise gauge is used in the same way as the marking gauge, but it has two spurs that can be adjusted to the required width of the mortise or tenon to be marked out.

Odd-leg calipers

These can be used on metal or plastic to draw a line along the length of the material, parallel to an edge.

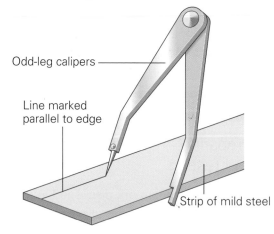

Figure 6.7 Odd-leg calipers

Mitre square

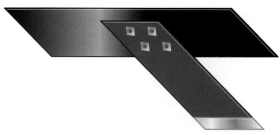

Figure 6.8 Mitre square

The mitre square can be used on wood or plastic to mark out or test angles of 45 or 135 degrees.

Sliding bevel

This can be used on wood, metal or plastic. The blade can be set to any angle, using a protractor, and tightened in position.

ACTIVITY

Ask your teacher if you could have some short ends of a variety of tube and bar. Use the inside and outside calipers to measure their diameters.

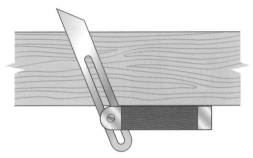

Figure 6.9 Sliding bevel

Inside and outside calipers

Inside calipers are used to measure the inside diameters of tube. Outside calipers are used to measure the outside diameters of tube or bar.

Centre square

This is used to find the centre on round bar. If you draw two lines across the end of the bar using the centre square, where the lines bisect is the centre.

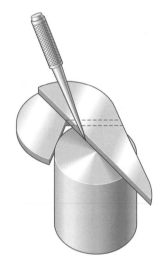

Figure 6.11 Centre square

Combination square

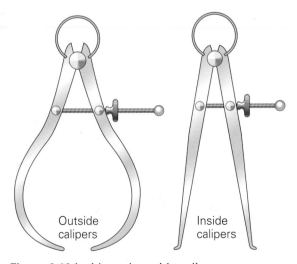

Outside calipers

Inside calipers

Figure 6.10 Inside and outside calipers

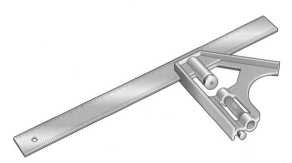

Figure 6.12 Combination square

As its name suggests, this tool will perform a variety of tasks, including measuring like a rule, measuring angles and depths, and checking for squareness over edges.

Centre and dot punches

These punches are used on metal and plastic. The centre punch is used to mark the centre of the hole to be drilled, while a dot punch is used to mark the centres of circles and arcs that will be marked out. The dot punch is also used to highlight lines to be cut.

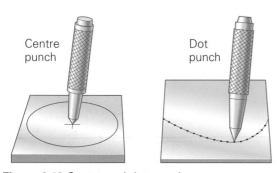

Centre punch

Dot punch

Figure 6.13 Centre and dot punches

Dividers

Dividers can be used to mark circles and arcs on metal and plastic.

Figure 6.14 Dividers

Micrometers

The micrometer is used to provide measurements with great precision. The external micrometer can measure accurately to 0.01 mm. There are also electronic digital micrometers that give you the reading automatically.

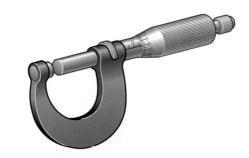

Figure 6.15 Micrometer

Figure 6.16 Electronic digital micrometer

QUESTION

Look at the drawing of the micrometer in Figure 6.17 and state the exact reading, shown to one hundredth of a millimetre (0.01 mm).

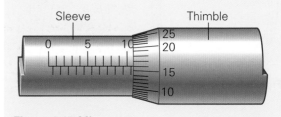

Sleeve

Thimble

Figure 6.17 Micrometer

Surface plate marking out

A surface plate provides a flat datum surface from which very accurate measurements can be taken. The workpiece can be held against an angle plate or clamped in a vee block while being marked out using a surface gauge.

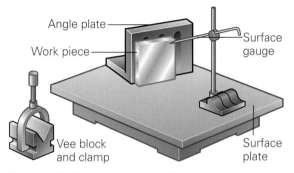

Figure 6.18 Surface plate marking out

Gauges

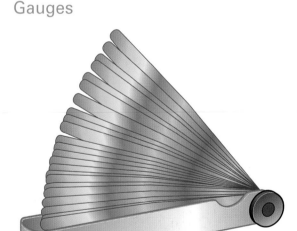

Figure 6.19 Feeler gauge

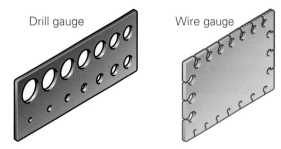

Figure 6.20 Drill and wire gauges

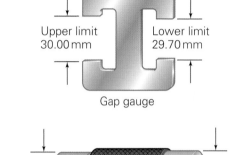

Figure 6.21 Plug and gap gauges

Feeler gauges are sets of steel blades ranging in thickness from 0.3 to 1.00 mm. The thickness is marked on each blade. The blades, or 'feelers', can be used singly or in combinations to make up a specific size. The feelers fit a gap when there is a slight pull when removing them from the clearance.

Wire gauges are used to measure the thickness of wire and, more commonly, sheet metal.

Drill gauges are used to find out the diameter of drills and round bar.

Templates

Templates can be used to draw or cut round unusual shapes or when a shape has to be repeated for batch production. Templates can be made quickly from paper or card, but more hard-wearing materials such as thin sheet wood, metal or plastic are used in industry when the template may be used many times.

KEY TERM

DATUM FACES – Sides, edges or ends of material that are perfectly flat and are used to measure or mark out from, ensuring that all measurements are accurate.

▶ Wasting

Wasting is concerned with the way that material is removed by cutting pieces off or cutting pieces out.

EXAMINER'S TIPS

Examiners often ask students to name a wasting process that could be carried out by hand or using a machine.

It is important that you know which tools or items of equipment are used. This will include the method of holding the work securely while carrying out wasting processes.

ACTIVITY

Complete a table similar to that shown below, listing as many different measuring, marking-out or testing tools and equipment as possible. Show the combination of materials that each could be used on and put a tick in the end column if you have used the tool or equipment.

Measuring, marking-out or testing tool or equipment	Wood	Metal	Plastic	Have I used it?
Steel rule	✓	✓	✓	✓
Try square	✓	✓	✓	✓

Table 6.2

▶ Sawing

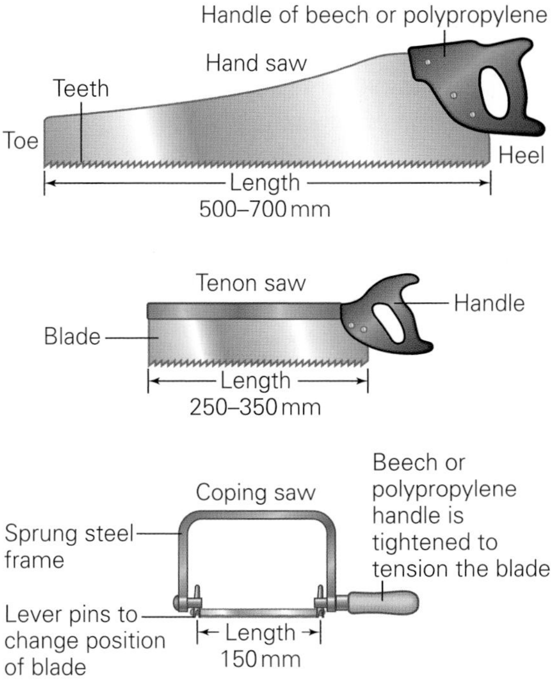

Handle of beech or polypropylene

Hand saw

Teeth

Toe

Heel

Length
500–700 mm

Tenon saw

Handle

Blade

Length
250–350 mm

Coping saw

Beech or
polypropylene
handle is
tightened to
tension the blade

Sprung steel
frame

Lever pins to
change position
of blade

Length
150 mm

Figure 6.22 Hand saw, tenon saw and coping saw

Handsaw

Handsaw is the general name for saws used to saw along or across the grain of large pieces of wood. The ripsaw is used along the grain, while the cross-cut saw is used to cut across the grain.

Tenon saws

Tenon saws are a general-purpose saw. You are likely to have used this saw more than any other as it is very good at making straight cuts in wood.

Coping saws

These are used to cut curves in thin wood and plastic. Care must be taken when using them because the blades can be broken quite easily. The blade should be fitted so that the teeth point backwards.

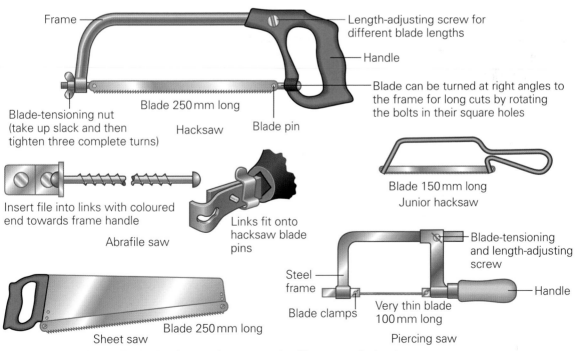

Frame

Length-adjusting screw for
different blade lengths

Handle

Blade can be turned at right angles to
the frame for long cuts by rotating
the bolts in their square holes

Blade 250 mm long

Hacksaw

Blade pin

Blade-tensioning nut
(take up slack and then
tighten three complete turns)

Blade 150 mm long
Junior hacksaw

Insert file into links with coloured
end towards frame handle

Abrafile saw

Links fit onto
hacksaw blade
pins

Blade-tensioning
and length-adjusting
screw

Steel
frame

Handle

Blade clamps

Very thin blade
100 mm long

Blade 250 mm long

Sheet saw

Piercing saw

Figure 6.23 Hacksaw, junior hacksaw, sheet saw, abrafile saw and piercing saw

Hacksaws

These are used to make straight cuts in metal. The blade is held tightly in the frame, with the teeth pointing forwards.

Junior hacksaws

Junion hacksaws are used in exactly the same way as the hacksaw, but on lighter or smaller-scale work. Both hacksaws can be used to cut plastic with care.

Sheet saws

Sheet saws are a combination of a handsaw and a hacksaw, which makes them very good for cutting sheet wood, metal or plastic.

Abrafile saw 'blades'

These are designed to fit into a hacksaw frame. The round 'blade' can be used to cut curves in wood, metal and plastic.

Piercing saws

Piercing saws are used for fine, intricate jewellery work, usually in metal, but they can be used to cut plastics. The blades have extremely fine teeth which can be broken easily if misused.

Scroll saw

Figure 6.24 Scroll saw

Machine saws such as the scroll saw are very versatile.

Jigsaw

The jigsaw is extremely useful for cutting shapes from sheet material and has the advantage of being portable. Blades for both saws are interchangeable for wood, metal and plastic, and are available in fine, medium and coarse grades for different purposes.

Figure 6.25 Jigsaw

▶ Methods of holding work securely

Wood that is sawn using a handsaw or a jigsaw would usually be held across a workbench because of the size of wood being sawn.

When using tenon and coping saws, the woodworker's vice would be used to secure the workpiece. A bench hook can also be used to cut small section pieces of wood. An engineer's vice is used when working with a hacksaw or an abrafile saw. Sometimes it is useful to clamp work flat onto a cutting board on a workbench. The cutting board prevents

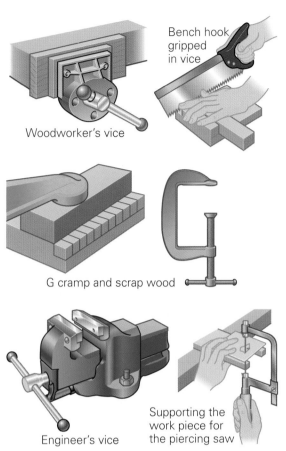

Woodworker's vice

Bench hook gripped in vice

G cramp and scrap wood

Engineer's vice

Supporting the work piece for the piercing saw

Figure 6.26 Methods of holding work securely

the saw blade from damaging the bench, while the scrap wood can be used as a guide for the blade and prevent bruising to the wooden workpiece. The metal cut when using the piercing saw would be supported over the edge of a workbench.

Drilling

There are many different types of drills and bits used when drilling holes in wood, metal and plastics. The drills and bits can be held in a drilling machine, a portable drill, a brace or a centre lathe.

Twist drills

Twist drills are used for drilling holes in wood, metal and plastic. Straight shanks fit into the chuck of a drilling machine, while morse-taper shanks fit directly into the drilling machine spindles and centre lathe tailstocks.

Countersink drills

Countersink drills provide the countersunk shape for screws.

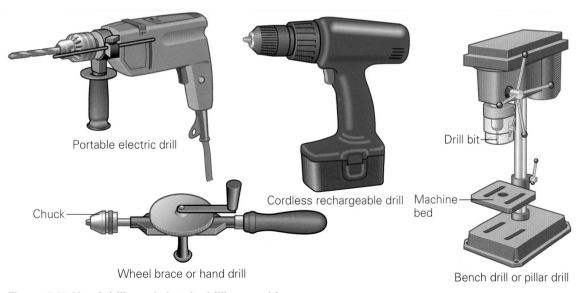

Portable electric drill

Cordless rechargeable drill

Drill bit

Chuck

Wheel brace or hand drill

Machine bed

Bench drill or pillar drill

Figure 6.27 Hand drills and electric drilling machines

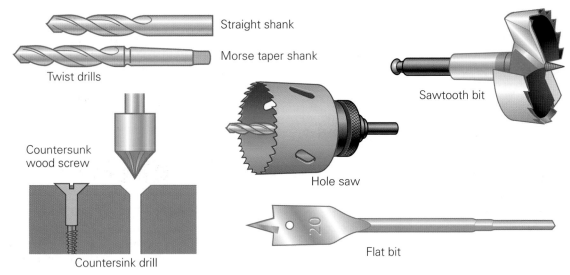

Figure 6.28 Drills and bits fitting into chucks of hand drills and electric drilling machines

Flat bits

These provide fast and accurate drilling in solid wood. The point is positioned before the drill is switched on and is left in the wood until the drill stops.

Hole saws

Hole saws enable you to drill holes 20–75 mm diameter. The hole saw has interchangeable cutters and removes the wood in the shape of a flat washer.

Sawtooth bits

Sawtooth bits will drill out smooth-sided, flat-bottomed holes quickly and efficiently.

Centre bits

Centre bits are used for boring shallow holes in wood. They are unsuitable for deep holes because they have no auger (flute) to take away the waste and no parallel sides to guide it.

Jennings auger bits

Jennings auger bits, or twist bits, are designed for drilling deep holes.

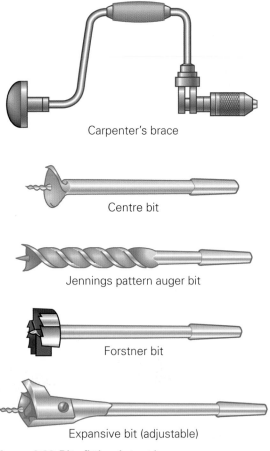

Figure 6.29 Bits fitting into a brace

Forstner bits

These are guided by their rim rather than a centre point. They provide smooth-sided, flat-bottomed holes.

Expansive bits

Expansive bits can be adjusted to drill shallow holes in wood 12–150 mm diameter.

Centre drill

A centre drill is used in a centre lathe to provide a 'start' when drilling into the end of a bar.

Advice when drilling/boring holes

- Make sure that the work is secure. Do not hold work with your fingers when using the drilling machine.

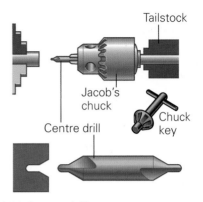

Figure 6.30 Centre drill

- If you are drilling straight through material, place scrap wood underneath to drill into.
- Make sure that the drill is tight in the chuck, remove the key and ensure that the safety guard is in place.

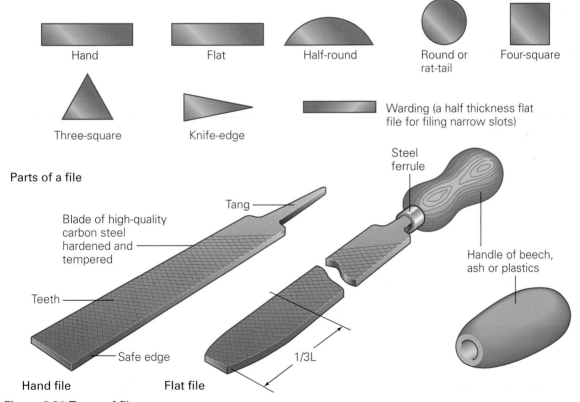

Figure 6.31 Types of files

- Centre-punch metal before drilling to prevent the drill tip from 'wandering'.
- Generally, the larger the drill, the slower the speed; the smaller the drill, the faster the speed.
- When drilling large-diameter holes, drill a 'pilot' hole first.

▶ Filing

Files are made from hardened and tempered high-carbon steel. They have rows of small teeth that work like very small chisels to produce 'filings'. Files are used to shape and smooth mainly metal, plastics and wood.

Files are classified by length, shape and cut of teeth. There are various grades of cut: rough and bastard cuts for coarse work; second cut for general use; and smooth and dead smooth for very fine work before polishing.

The shape of each file is designed to be used to produce a similar shape on the material it is cutting.

Hand file

The hand file has a **safe edge** (without any teeth) that allows it to file in a 90-degree corner without removal of material on the vertical surface.

Needle file

Needle files are used for intricate work. They have dead-smooth cuts and are available in a wide variety of shapes for different purposes.

Teeth   Knurled handle

Figure 6.32 Needle file

Surform tools

Surform tools have a cutting action similar to a cheese grater. They can remove wood very quickly. The most common shaped blades are flat, curved and round.

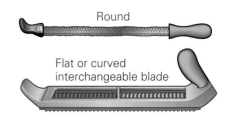

Round

Flat or curved
interchangeable blade

Figure 6.33 Surform tools

Methods of filing

Cross filing uses the full length of the file and is used to remove waste material quickly. It does not leave a smooth surface.

Draw filing is used to produce a smooth surface after cross filing. Only part of the file is used and very little material is removed.

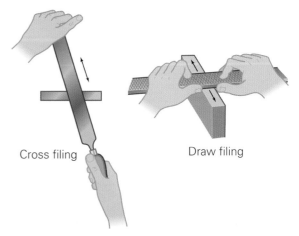

Cross filing   Draw filing

Figure 6.34 Methods of filing

▶ Chiselling

Chisels are used to cut and shape wood. You are likely to have used a chisel when cutting a joint in wood.

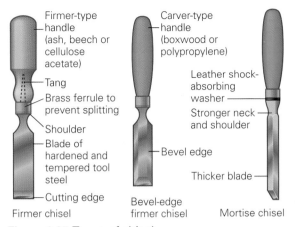

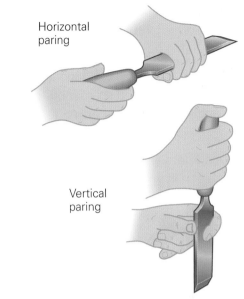

Figure 6.35 Types of chisel

Firmer chisel
The firmer chisel is a general-purpose chisel that can withstand light blows from a mallet.

Bevel-edge chisel
The bevel-edge chisel is different from the firmer chisel in that it has bevelled or sloping edges that allow it to be used in acute-angle corners, for example when cutting out a dovetail joint.

Mortise chisel
The mortise chisel is designed to be hit with a mallet. It has a thicker blade than the other chisels, which allows it to lever out waste wood without it breaking.

Methods of chiselling
Paring describes how chisels are used with hand pressure only. Safety is essential, and the most important rule is that you must keep both hands behind the cutting edge of the chisel at all times.

Horizontal paring would be used with the wood secured in a vice. It is good practice to rest the chisel on the top of the vice when paring. You would use horizontal paring to cut out a halving or housing joint.

Figure 6.36 Horizontal and vertical paring

Vertical paring from above requires considerable pressure and a G cramp is used to secure the wood. You may need to use a mallet to provide enough force to cut through the fibres of the wood.

▶ Planing

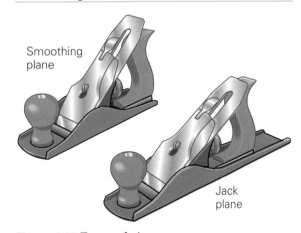

Figure 6.37 Types of plane

Jack planes
Jack planes are 350 mm long and are used for the quick removal of waste wood to

make surfaces flat and to achieve the required size.

Smoothing planes

Smoothing planes are 250 mm long and have a blade that is ground and sharpened for fine finishing and for planing end grain.

Special planes

There are numerous 'special' planes that you may have seen in your workshop.

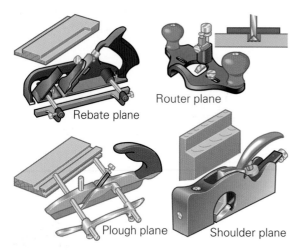

Figure 6.38 Special planes

Rebate planes cut out rebates. A stopped rebate can only be partly cut out with a plane. A small area would need to be chiselled out first to allow the plane to stop before planing right through.

Router planes are used to cut out housings across the grain of wood. They are also used to level the bottom of housings.

Plough planes are used to cut grooves and rebates.

Shoulder planes are used to clean up and level the shoulders of joints.

How a plane works

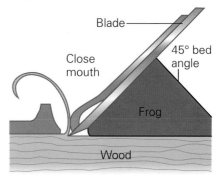

Figure 6.39 Jack plane blade

The cutting action of a plane is similar to that of a chisel held in a frame at a specific angle. Plane blades need to be ground, sharpened and set accurately for them to work effectively. If you think the plane you are using is not cutting properly, ask your teacher to check it rather than adjusting it yourself.

Methods of planing

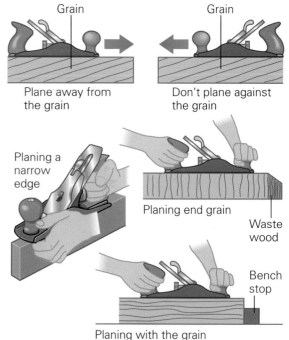

Figure 6.40 Methods of planing

Always plane along the grain; otherwise you will tear the surface of the wood. To find out which way the grain is running, look at an edge and follow the grain markings to the surface.

When planing an edge it is important to secure the wood in a vice.

When planing long thin strips of wood, use a bench stop, as the bench itself will support the strip and stop it from bending.

End grain poses problems because of the danger of splitting if the plane is taken straight across the end of the wood. One method of preventing this is to tighten a piece of scrap wood of the same thickness at one end, allowing you to plane right across. A second method is to plane to the middle of the wood, stop, and then plane to the middle from the other end. This method only works on wide boards as it can be difficult to control and stop the plane.

Centre-lathe turning

Centre lathes are used to make round components from metal and plastic. The workpiece is held securely and rotates while a single-point cutting tool cuts the material. The material can also be drilled when a drill is locked in the tailstock.

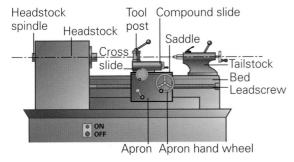

Figure 6.41 Centre lathe

The four main parts of the centre lathe are:

1. Bed – on which the other parts are positioned.
2. Headstock – containing the gearbox used to drive the workpiece.
3. Tailstock – where drill chucks can be inserted and for supporting long workpieces.
4. Saddle – which, as its name suggests, fits over the bed of the lathe and moves along it, carrying the cross slide and the tool post.

Holding work securely

The three-jaw self-centring chuck secures round or hexagonal materials. The three jaws come together automatically to tighten around the workpiece. Similar chucks are used in hand drills and drilling machines.

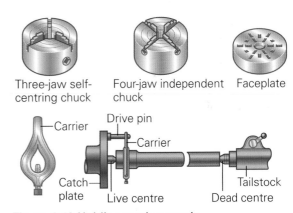

Figure 6.42 Holding work securely

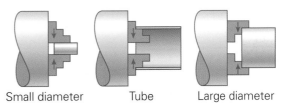

Figure 6.43 Holding work in a three-jaw self-centring chuck

The four-jaw independent chuck is used to secure square or irregular-shaped material. Each jaw is tightened individually. Checking that the workpiece is rotating truly takes time, and therefore it is better if the turning operation can be carried out at one session rather than having to realign the material in the chuck.

The faceplate has a series of slots and holes to enable irregular-shaped work to be bolted to it.

Long pieces of work can be turned 'between centres'. The workpiece must first be faced off to make it flat, and then centre-drilled so that the 'dead' centre (the centre that does not move) and the 'live' centre (the centre that drives the workpiece) can be located and tightened.

The three-jaw chuck is the most commonly used and is very versatile. This chuck has two sets of three jaws. One set of jaws is used for small-diameter material and tube that can be secured on its inside surface. A second set of jaws enables large-diameter work to be held securely.

Lathe tools

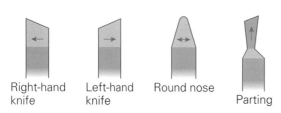

Figure 6.44 Lathe tools

Knife tools are used to face off, cut shoulders on work or cut material off along the length of the workpiece. There are right- and left-handed versions, depending on the direction you are working from.

Round-nosed tools can be used for left-to-right or right-to-left turning and also enable rounded or radiused corners to be cut.

Parting tools are used to make grooves in the workpiece or to cut it off.

Figure 6.45 Setting lathe tools to the correct height

Lathework operations

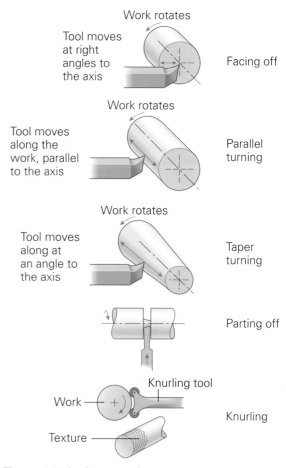

Figure 6.46 Lathe operations

Material	Cutting speed (m/min)	Cutting fluid/lubricant
Aluminium	300	None or paraffin
Brass	90	None
Mild steel	30	Soluble oil
Cast iron	20	None
Tool steel	15	Soluble oil
Nylon	200	None
Acrylic	200	None

Table 6.3 Cutting speeds and lubrication

Facing off is where the tool moves across the end of the workpiece at 90 degrees to make a flat surface.

Parallel turning is where the tool moves along the length of the workpiece to produce a round shape.

Taper turning is where the tool moves along the length of the work to produce a conical shape. Taper turning is also used to produce chamfers.

Parting off is where the tool is used to cut grooves or to cut off the workpiece. Care is needed when carrying out these operations – the tool should be 'fed' slowly, withdrawn and moved along before reinserting it.

Knurling is where a tool is 'pressed' against the surface of the workpiece to produce a diamond-knurled surface. The tool has two very hard wheels pivoted in a swivelling head.

Wood-turning lathe

There are two types of turning that can be carried out on a wood-turning lathe:

- between-centres turning
- faceplate turning.

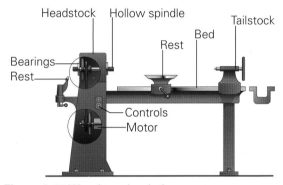

Figure 6.47 Wood-turning lathe

Between-centres turning

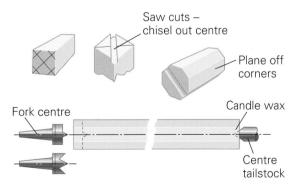

Figure 6.48 Between-centres turning

Between-centres turning is used to make products such as chair or stool legs and rolling pins.

A fork centre is pushed into the spindle in the headstock; this drives the workpiece as it is connected directly to the motor. In the tailstock, a dead centre is pushed in; this simply supports the workpiece while it rotates. The workpiece needs to be prepared before it can be mounted on the lathe. A saw cut is made in one end of the wood so that the fork centre can fit tightly to drive the wood. The edges of the wood are planed off to make turning easier to start and to prevent splitting.

Faceplate turning

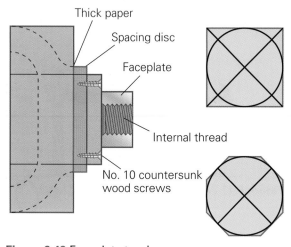

Figure 6.49 Faceplate turning

Faceplate turning is used to make products such as bowls.

The workpiece should have the corners removed to help the start of turning. It is then glued to a similar size and shape of scrap wood with thick paper sandwiched in between. This is then screwed onto a faceplate. The faceplate with the wood attached can then be screwed onto the headstock spindle, ready to turn.

Advice when using a wood-turning lathe

- The tool rest must be as close to the workpiece as possible. Always spin the work by hand to make sure that it does not 'catch' the tool rest.

- Lathe speeds are generally as follows: the larger the diameter of wood to be turned, the slower the speed; the smaller the diameter, the faster the speed.

- Scrapers are the safest type of turning tool to use. Gouges require more care and skill.

- Use outside calipers to test the diameter required. On complicated shapes it is best to use a template.

▶ Screw cutting

There are two types of screw cutting:

- **Threading** is the term to describe screw threads cut on the outside of round rod. This is done by means of a circular split die held in a diestock.

- **Tapping** is the term used to describe screw threads cut on the inside of tube. This is done by means of taps held in a tap wrench.

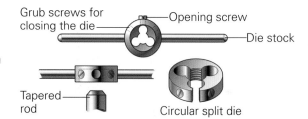

Figure 6.50 Diestock and die

Threading

1. When starting, always try to press down firmly and squarely to avoid a 'drunken' thread.

2. Use the appropriate lubricant.

3. Chamfer the end of the rod to make it easier to start cutting the thread.

4. Fit the circular split die into the diestock with the size information showing.

5. Tighten the middle screw to open the die for the first cut.

6. Tighten the two outer screws for the next cut if you find that the thread is too tight a fit when screwed into the inside thread.

7. When applying pressure to cut into the material, you will need to turn or 'ease back' the die to break off the swarf and remove the cuttings.

Tapping

This is exactly the same process except that three taps may need to be used.

The taper tap is used to make it easier when starting and can be used on its own in thin material.

The second tap is used to make threads started by the taper tap deeper.

The plug tap is used to cut full threads in 'blind' holes and in thicker material.

Taps are made from high-speed steel (HSS). They are very brittle, so you will need to be very careful when using them.

Remember that the tapping drill size will be slightly smaller than the size of screw thread to cut.

Table 6.4 shows some tapping drill sizes.

Screw thread size	Tapping drill size
M2	1.6
M3	2.5
M4	3.3
M5	4.2
M6	5.0
M8	6.8
M10	8.5
M12	10.2

Table 6.4 Tapping drill sizes

▶ Shearing

Shearing is the action of tinsnips or bench shears when cutting sheet metal. It is similar to that of a pair of scissors, with one blade passing another.

Tinsnips and bench shears will cut through aluminium, copper and even thin mild steel sheet.

Figure 6.51 Tap wrench and taps

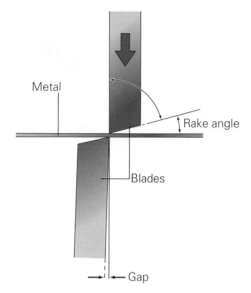

Figure 6.52 Shearing action

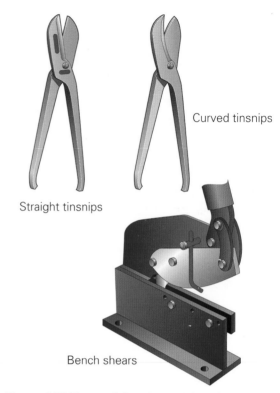

Figure 6.53 Types of tinsnips and bench shears

Tinsnips

When using tinsnips, make sure that the sheet metal is pushed right back between the two blades. If you only use the end of the blades there is a possibility that you will twist the metal. Often one handle is secured in an engineer's vice and the sheet metal is fed between the blades, with pressure placed on the movable handle.

Bench shears

These can be used to cut thin rod and strip as well as sheet metal. The long handle of the bench shears provides a lot more leverage than tinsnips.

Cold chisels

Cold chisels can shear sheet metal when it is secured in a vice.

Cold chisels are made from high-carbon steel, have a cutting edge ground to a 60-degree angle, are at least 100 mm long and vary from 6 to 25 mm wide.

The chisel is held at 30 degrees to the workpiece, with one side of it resting on the vice, while a cut is made on the waste side of the line.

Figure 6.54 Cutting sheet metal in a vice

▶ Blanking and piercing

Blanking is the operation of cutting out a piece of metal of the required shape by using a punch and a die. In this case, it is the removed piece of metal that is important and not the hole produced.

Piercing is the operation of producing a hole of any shape in a sheet of metal, using a punch and a die. The material removed is unimportant and is treated as scrap. 'Punching' is similar to piercing, but refers to the production of a circular hole.

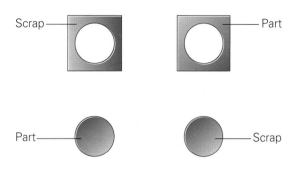

Figure 6.55 Blanking and piercing/punching

KEY TERM

WASTING – This refers to the way that material is removed by cutting pieces off or cutting pieces out.

SAFE EDGE – The hand file has a safe edge (without any teeth) that allows it to file in a 90-degree corner without removal of material on the vertical surface.

CROSS FILING – This method uses the full length of the file and is used to remove waste material quickly. It does not leave a smooth surface.

DRAW FILING – This is used to produce a smooth surface after cross filing. Only part of the file is used and very little material is removed.

FACING OFF – This refers to the tool moving across the end of the workpiece at 90 degrees to make a flat surface.

PARALLEL TURNING – Where the tool moves along the length of the workpiece to produce a round shape.

TAPER TURNING – Where the tool moves along the length of the work to produce a conical shape. Taper turning is also used to produce chamfers.

PARTING OFF – This is where the tool is used to make grooves or to cut off the workpiece.

KNURLING – This is where a tool is 'pressed' against the surface of the workpiece to produce a diamond-knurled surface. The tool has two very hard wheels pivoted in a swivelling head.

BETWEEN-CENTRES TURNING – This is used to make products such as chair or stool legs and rolling pins.

FACEPLATE TURNING – This is used to make products such as bowls.

THREADING – A term used to describe screw threads cut on the outside of round rod.

TAPPING – A term used to describe screw threads cut on the inside of tube.

SHEARING – Refers to the action of tinsnips or bench shears when cutting sheet metal. It is similar to that of a pair of scissors, with one blade passing another.
BLANKING – This is the operation of cutting out a piece of metal of the required shape by using a punch and a die. It is the removed piece of metal that is important and not the hole produced.
PIERCING – This is the operation of producing a hole of any shape in a sheet of metal, using a punch and a die. The material removed is unimportant and is treated as scrap.

QUESTIONS

1. Name the tools used to:
   - mark out the line
   - remove the waste wood.

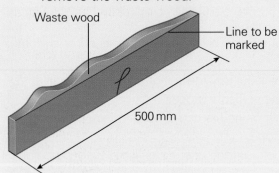

Figure 6.56 Length of wood marked out to be planed to width

2. Name the marking-out tools used when the material is:
   - metal
   - wood.

3. Name the tools used to remove the waste when the material is:
   - metal
   - wood.

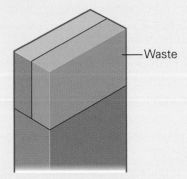

Figure 6.57

Systems to improve and ensure accuracy of making

These include jigs, fixtures, templates and patterns, which are all used to control accuracy when manufacturing products in quantity. They can also be used to control accuracy in the manufacture of single products if the product has a number of identical components. There is a subtle difference between a jig and a fixture. Technically, a jig is used to guide a tool, for example a drill or saw, while a fixture is the means of holding the work in place. Some examples of jigs, formers and templates and patterns with specific uses are shown below.

Jigs

Jigs are 3D devices that can be used to assist the manufacturing process when sawing, drilling, bending and shaping.

EXAMINER'S TIP

The 'good features' given for each device below are what examiners are looking for in your answers in the written exam.

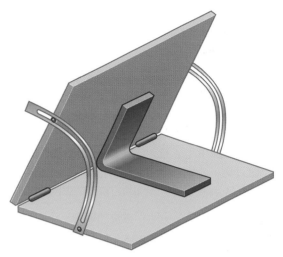

Figure 6.59 Bending jig

- The plastic can be pushed into the angle easily.
- The same angle can be achieved every time.

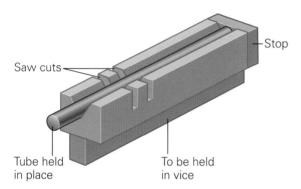

Figure 6.58 Sawing jig

The sawing jig has the following good features:

- The tube to be cut is held securely in place.
- Part of the jig can fit into a vice to prevent it from moving about.
- Identical lengths can be sawn, due to the position of the saw cuts.
- It is straightforward to use.

The bending jig, used to produce the internal bend in the sheet plastic, has the following good features:

- It is adjustable to any angle between 0 and 90 degrees.
- It can be adjusted quickly and easily.

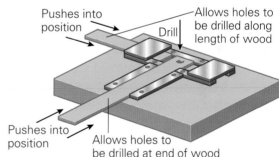

Figure 6.60 Drilling jig

The drilling jig has the following good features:

- The jig fits quickly and easily over a drilling machine table.
- Strips of wood can be pushed into the jig and are held safely while being drilled.
- The holes can be drilled at the end of a strip or along its length, depending on which 'guide' is used.

- The holes will be drilled in the same place every time.

Templates

Templates are the best way to mark out irregular or awkward shapes. Any thin, fairly rigid material is suitable. Thick card, for example, could be used to mark a small batch of products. If the scale of manufacture is larger, then a more durable material such as manufactured board or thin metal sheet would be better.

Using a template, a shape can be marked out quickly and accurately on sheet material. Some templates require greater accuracy, for example when marking out positions for constructions. In this case, it would be essential for the template to have some form of lipping that fitted up against at least two

edges, to ensure the correct location every time.

Patterns

If you were to cut out an ornate part of some stage scenery from a sheet of plywood, it would be easier to cut the shape out of paper or thin card first and then glue it onto the plywood. You could then use the pattern to give you the outline of the shape required.

KEY TERM

JIGS are 3D devices that can be used to assist the manufacturing process when sawing, drilling, bending and shaping.

6.9 KNOWLEDGE AND UNDERSTANDING OF BASIC EQUIPMENT

Imagine a workshop situation. Your teacher asks you to get a length of mild steel tube from the storeroom and cut off a piece 400 mm long. You have learnt about measuring, marking out and sawing different materials during your design and technology course, and now is the time to put it into practice. You should be able to:

- know which tools you need and recognise them
- name the tools
- use them safely and effectively.

In addition, you should be able to carry out a similar task, but on a length of 50 x 25 mm pine.

EXAMINER'S TIP

Examiners often ask students to name tools and equipment they would use to carry out a specific task. They also expect you to describe the safety precautions associated with those tools and equipment.

6.10 AWARENESS OF ALTERNATIVE TOOLS AND EQUIPMENT

Think about the previous example of sawing a length of 50 x 25 mm pine. You correctly named a tenon saw and you held the work securely against a bench stop. But there are alternative methods: you could have taken the length of pine to a Hegner saw and cut it quickly and accurately.

Think about the different ways of removing metal – using a cold chisel, hacksaw or even bench shears, depending on the size of the material.

EXAMINER'S TIP

Examiners often ask students to describe two methods of carrying out the same task. Sometimes they may require an answer that describes a 'hand' method and a 'machine' method.

CHAPTER 7

SYSTEMS AND PROCESSES

By the end of this chapter you should have developed a knowledge and understanding of the:

- systems and processes used to bend and form resistant materials
- systems and processes used to join resistant materials
- finishing processes used to protect and improve the performance and appearance of resistant materials.

This chapter deals with a range of processes used to work, form, join and finish wood, metal and plastics. The knowledge you will develop will help you successfully complete the controlled assessment task (CAT) and prepare you for the written examination. Your knowledge and understanding of systems and processes are specifically tested in Question 7 of the exam.

7.1 BENDING AND FORMING RESISTANT MATERIALS

Wood

KEY POINT

- The number of processes that can be used to deform wood is very limited because of the nature of the material. Wood will only bend by a very small amount before it breaks and this makes forming very difficult. As wood cuts more easily than other resistant materials, it is common for wood products to be made by machining (a wasting process).

Bending

A very basic method of bending wood into curves is called **kerfing**, which involves putting a series of evenly spaced saw cuts in the timber to allow it to be bent. It is only really suitable if just one side of the curve is to be visible, such as for the curved side of a guitar body. As the wood is bent into a curve, the edges of the saw cuts close up to each other and a smooth curve is produced on the outside of the bend.

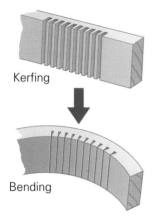

Kerfing

Bending

Figure 7.1 Kerfing wood

One method of deforming wood that has been used for many years is **steam bending**. This involves placing the wood in a sealed chest which is kept filled with steam at 100°C so that the wood absorbs the hot moisture and becomes softer and easy to bend. The amount of time needed to soften the wood sufficiently for bending depends on the timber being used, but most timbers are steamed for one hour for every 25 mm of thickness before they are taken out for bending.

The steamed wood is bent into the required shape around a special **former** and clamped firmly in place so that it keeps its shape while it dries out. The shaped wood needs to dry out thoroughly before it is unclamped, otherwise it is likely to twist as further drying takes place.

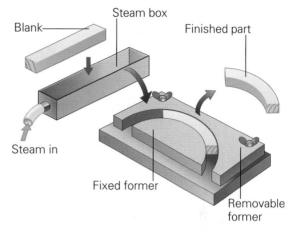

Figure 7.2 Steam bending timber

Laminating

Another more commonly used method of producing 'bent wood' shapes is **laminating**, in which the shape required is built up from thin layers of wood called veneers. In this way, any thickness can be produced and tighter bends can be achieved than by steaming solid timber. The layers of veneer are glued together, using one of the many strong modern adhesives available, and then clamped around a former until the adhesive is set. The method used to clamp the laminated shape depends on the size and complexity of the shape being produced and the number required. Typical clamping arrangements include specially shaped blocks, standard G or sash cramps, flexible steel bands and vacuum bags. Care must be taken to ensure that the laminated shape does not become glued to the former, and it is normal to use wax on the formers to stop the adhesive sticking to them, or to place thin rubber strips between the shape and the formers.

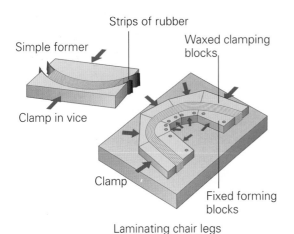

Laminating chair legs

Figure 7.3 Forming laminated wooden shapes

The construction of the shaped form looks quite similar to plywood, but the grain of each layer of veneer runs in the same direction, following the shape of the curve, whereas with plywood the grains of alternate layers run at 90 degrees to each other.

KEY TERMS

KERFING – Making saw cuts so that wood can bend.
STEAM BENDING – Softening the fibres of wood with steam to allow it to bend.
FORMER – A block made to hold material in the shape required.
LAMINATING – Building up a shape in thin layers.

ACTIVITY

Figure 7.4 Mahogany chair

The back legs of the mahogany chair in Figure 7.4 are curved to make the chair more stable and to improve its appearance. Use sketches and notes to explain how the legs could be shaped if:

(a) They were made from solid mahogany.
(b) They were made from pine and covered with a mahogany veneer.

In each case, the legs must be made by forming and not by cutting the shape out of a larger piece of wood.

EXAMINER'S TIPS

If an examination question asks you to use sketches and notes in your answer, always make sure that you use both. The notes (annotation) help you to explain more clearly what it is that your sketch shows.

▶ Metal

KEY POINT

- Unlike wood, most metals are malleable or can be made more malleable by using heat. This means that they can be deformed without cracking, and shaped metal parts can be produced by a number of processes.

Bending

Simple bends can be produced by holding the metal in a bench vice and hammering it into shape. Depending on the metal and its thickness, this can be done either hot or cold, and thinner metal sections can often be bent by hand. When bending non-ferrous metals such as copper, brass and aluminium, the metal is often annealed before bending, to make it more malleable.

If an accurate bend or a particular shape is required, this is done using a specially made former. When a number of items need to be bent to the same shape, a bending jig should be made to ensure that they are all accurately made.

Where very large numbers of parts are needed, special-purpose machines are often built to make them. All the curved parts on the stainless-steel bench shown in Figure 7.5 are made by forcing the metal strip round formers, using hydraulic pressure to produce the high force required to bend it. The machine is only used for the parts for this bench, but it can be used to make thousands of identical parts.

Figure 7.6 Stainless-steel bench

Beaten metalwork processes

The most commonly used **beaten metalwork** processes are hollowing, sinking and raising, although some shapes in copper and brass are formed by folding or rolling flat sheet metal and then silver-soldering the edges to produce a seam. This is often used to produce cylinders, but it is also the best way to form straight-sided items.

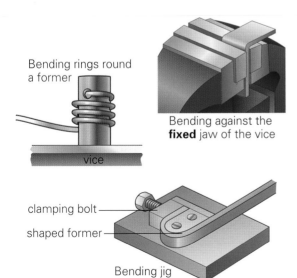

Bending rings round a former

vice

Bending against the **fixed** jaw of the vice

clamping bolt

shaped former

Bending jig

Figure 7.5 Examples of metal bending

KEY POINT

- Non-ferrous metals, such as copper, brass and aluminium, can be formed into shape using beaten sheet-metal working methods, to produce items such as bowls, vases and jugs. Gold and silver are particularly suitable for this type of forming and were extensively used for many years, but they are very expensive to use, and base metals are now often plated to give the appearance of these precious metals.

Hollowing is used to produce shallow dishes and bowls and involves hammering the soft metal into a leather sandbag or a hollowed-out wooden block. This is done using an egg-shaped mallet called a bossing mallet that is normally made out of boxwood. A round disc of metal is cut from a sheet and then annealed to soften it. After cleaning the metal, concentric circles are drawn on the disc and the hollowing is started at the outside edge, working in, one circle at a time, to the centre.

Sinking is quite similar to hollowing and is also used to produce shallow dishes, but with

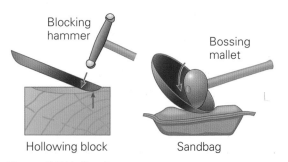

Figure 7.7 Hollowing

a flat rim round the top. It is carried out on a wooden block, specially shaped to give the required depth of the finished dish. Two pegs are fitted in the top of the sinking block to make sure the rim is the same width all the way round the dish. The annealed disc of metal is held against the pegs on the sinking block and hammered into the shaped part of the block using a round-faced metal blocking hammer or a boxwood mallet. The sinking is done gradually, working round the dish until the required depth is reached, and the rim is made flat after each round of sinking. Sinking is quite a slow process, and the metal usually needs to be annealed and cleaned several times during the forming of the dish.

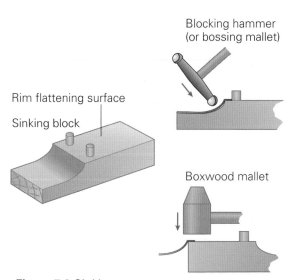

Figure 7.8 Sinking

Raising is carried out on shaped metal stakes. Although shallow bowls can be raised over round stakes, it is easier to make them by hollowing, and raising is normally used to form deeper items such as vases and jugs. The shape is usually started off by hollowing, but then continued using metal raising hammers on a raising stake. The shape required is made gradually deeper and narrower, working round the diameter at each stage.

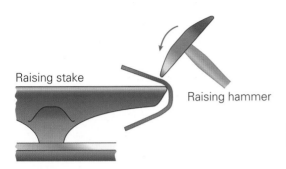

Figure 7.9 Raising

Whichever process is used to form the shaped item, it will need to be finished off by **planishing** to remove any irregularities in the shape and give a smooth, even surface. Planishing involves lightly hammering the metal against specially shaped and highly polished metal stakes, using polished planishing hammers. Each hammer blow needs to be of equal 'weight', and they should all slightly overlap each other. This leaves small facets on the surface of the metal which can be polished out or left as a decorative finish.

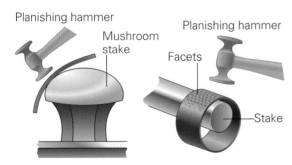

Figure 7.10 Planishing

These metal-beating processes are used for the one-off manufacture of handmade items and prototype models, as they are time consuming and require considerable practice and skill to carry out successfully. Where large-scale production of such items is needed, this is done using presswork operations to form the required shapes; some design changes may be necessary to enable the parts to be made by quantity production methods.

KEY TERMS

BEATEN METALWORK – Making shaped decorative items from non-ferrous metals.
HOLLOWING – Hammering softened metal into a sandbag or a hollowed-out wooden block.
SINKING – Hammering into a specially shaped wooden block to form a bowl with a flat rim.
RAISING – Making deeper items on polished metal stakes.
PLANISHING – Smoothing out surface imperfections with polished hammers and stakes.

Sheet metalwork

KEY POINT

- **Sheet metalwork** is used to produce hollow items such as air extraction ducts, boxes and trays from thin sheet metal, often only 1 mm thick. Many metals are suitable for use, but galvanised steel, aluminium and tinplate are the most common.

Before cutting the sheet metal to shape, a cardboard mock-up is made to check the shape, size and position of joining flaps. This is then used as the **net** (development) to mark out the required shape on the metal sheet, and cutting is done using hand shears (tinsnips), a bench shear or a power guillotine for larger parts.

Straight-sided objects can be folded in the vice or over wooden formers, and cylinders are produced in **bending rolls**. The metal should be protected by soft jaws if clamped in an engineer's vice, and any hammering must be done with a rawhide or nylon mallet to avoid leaving marks in the metal. Because the cut edges of the sheet metal are very sharp, a **safe edge** is normally produced by folding back a narrow flap of the material. This also stiffens the edge and helps the object to keep its shape.

Figure 7.11 Sheet metal working

When the metal has been cut to shape and folded or rolled, the joints are made by riveting, soldering or, in some cases, welding.

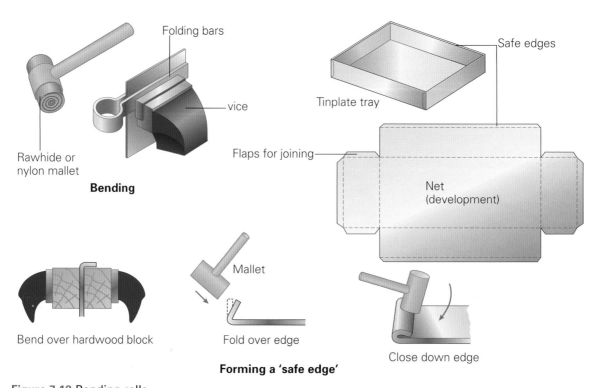

Figure 7.12 Bending rolls

On an industrial scale, items such as galvanised steel ducting are made on specially made semi-automatic machines. The metal is cut, shaped and joined on a flow-line basis, with much use being made of robots to carry out handling and joining processes.

Figure 7.13 Galvanised steel trunking

KEY TERM

SHEET METALWORK – Making hollow objects by folding, rolling and joining thin sheet metal.

Forging

KEY POINT

- **Forging** is generally considered as the process of forming metal while it is hot, although in modern industry some items can now be 'cold-forged' using very high-pressure hydraulics to 'squeeze' the metal into shape.

Hot-forging is one of the oldest methods of forming metals, and it is still used to produce shaped parts. It is particularly useful where strength is important, and steel is the metal most commonly used for forged parts. When forging, the grain of the metal is made to follow the shape of the item being produced and becomes more dense. This makes the item much stronger than cutting it from a solid block, as the grain is not interrupted and weakened.

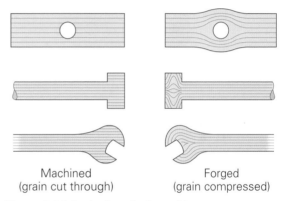

Machined
(grain cut through)   Forged
(grain compressed)

Figure 7.14 Grain flow in forged items

There are many different techniques used to forge metal, some of which are mainly used to produce decorative effects such as twists and scrolls. All the techniques require skilful use of the hammer and other blacksmith's tools in the workshop, and some have been modified for use in industry for large-scale production.

A wide range of special tools is used for particular forgework processes, but the three vital pieces of equipment for general work are the forge, the **anvil** and the hammer.

A blacksmith's forge traditionally burned coke to provide the heat, but modern ceramic chip forges are gas-fired. The metal to be heated is pushed into the bed of ceramic chips to prevent the air oxidising the hot metal.

The anvil is the most important piece of

equipment of all and is used for almost all forgework operations.

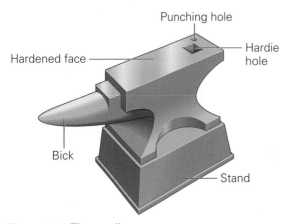

Figure 7.15 The anvil

The anvil is made from mild steel and has a hardened steel face for hammering the hot metal on. The square hardie hole at the back of the face is to hold the specially shaped tools used for certain operations, and the smaller round hole is for punching holes in hot metal. The shape of the bick allows curves to be formed round it, and the whole anvil is usually mounted on a stand or a large block of wood to bring it up to a comfortable working height.

Forgework operations

Upsetting (sometimes called 'jumping up') is used to increase the thickness of a bar at a particular point. The area to be 'upset' is heated to white-hot while keeping the rest of the bar cold. The bar is then hammered on the anvil or in a vice to spread the heated metal and increase the thickness. The finished bar with its upset section is then slightly shorter than the original.

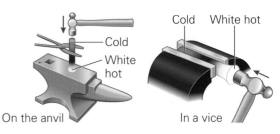

Figure 7.16 Upsetting

Upsetting is widely used in industry to form the heads of rivets, screws and bolts, when it is commonly referred to as heading. The process is highly automated to mass-produce the items and may be done either hot or cold, depending on the size and the metal used. Only the larger sizes are now made by 'hot' heading, as cold heading is quicker and gives a better finish. The material is fed to the automatic machine from a coil, cut to length and then transferred to a die. A specially shaped punch then forms the head on the end of the bar, and the finished item is ejected from the die to go on for threading if needed.

Scrolling and twisting operations are used to produce decorative features like those used in traditional wrought ironwork, although mild steel is now commonly used for this type of work. After heating the steel to bright red, the steel strip is thinned and bent over on the anvil before forming the scroll, which may be done on **cranking horns** or a special scrolling iron. A scroll may need to be reheated several times during the bending, but a twist should be completed in one operation from bright-red heat, turning the bar steadily with the twisting wrench.

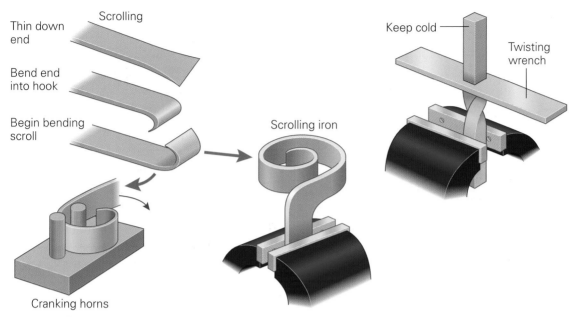

Thin down end

Scrolling

Keep cold

Twisting wrench

Bend end into hook

Begin bending scroll

Scrolling iron

Cranking horns

Figure 7.17 Scrolling and twisting

KEY TERMS

FORGING – Hammering or squeezing metal into shape, usually when hot.
ANVIL – The main piece of equipment for hand-forging metal.
UPSETTING – Increasing the thickness of part of a hot metal bar.
CRANKING HORNS – Simple tool for bending strip metal into curves.

▶ Plastics

Line bending

Line bending is the process used to produce simple bends in plastic sheet. It is particularly useful for forming acrylic sheet, which can be softened by heating it to about 160°C. The acrylic is heated along the line where the bend is to be made, and this is best done with a strip heater. The one shown in Figure 7.18 has a long electric element that is adjustable for height. The further away from the element the plastic is, the wider the softened strip will be, and then a more gradual bend can be produced. If the plastic

KEY POINT

- Thermoplastics are easy to form because they can be softened by heat; there are several forming processes that can be carried out in the school workshop using quite basic equipment. Because thermosetting plastics cannot be softened by heat, they are normally moulded directly into the shape required and cannot then be deformed. All the processes used to deform thermoplastics involve heating the plastic to make it softer, and it is very important that care is taken when using these processes.

is positioned too close to the heating element it can overheat and burn, causing 'blistering', which ruins the surface of the plastic. To prevent this overheating, the plastic sheet should be turned over frequently so that it is heated evenly from both sides.

Figure 7.18 An electric strip heater

When the plastic is soft enough to be flexible it will start to bend under its own weight, and it can then be removed using leather gloves and bent into shape. This is usually done using a specially shaped former or a bending jig to make sure the bend is made accurately. These need to have very smooth surfaces, otherwise any grain marks or defects could become imprinted in the soft plastic. It is important that the plastic is held against the former or jig until it has cooled down and becomes hard again, so that it sets in the correct position.

If larger curves and bends are required, a variation on the line-bending process can be used. This is called drape forming. The plastic sheet is usually heated in a temperature-controlled oven because of the width of the strip needing to be heated. The softened plastic is then 'draped' over a former, pulled tightly onto it using a length of cloth, and held there until the plastic has cooled, either by hand or using clamps.

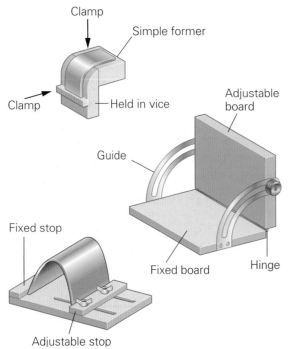

Figure 7.19 Line bending

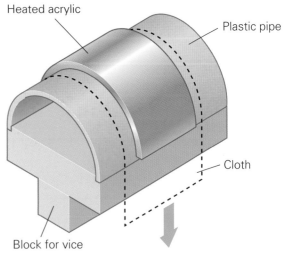

Figure 7.20 Drape forming

Press moulding

This process is used to produce more complex shapes, such as dishes and trays, where curves in more than one direction need to be formed. It can be used on thin acrylic sheet, and also on other thin-sheet plastic materials such as ABS (acrylonitrile-butadiene-styrene) and HIPS (high-impact polystyrene).

Press moulding involves the use of two-part formers, consisting of a plug to produce the shape required, and a yoke to press the soft plastic over the plug. The plug should have angled sides and smooth, rounded corners so that the finished moulding is easy to remove from it.

The hole in the yoke needs to be bigger than the size of the plug to allow for the thickness of the plastic sheet between them, leaving a gap of about one and a half times the thickness of the plastic.

The two-part former includes guide pegs to make sure the plug and yoke are aligned properly as the yoke is put in place.

The plastic sheet to be moulded needs to be heated in an oven so that the whole of it is soft and flexible. It is then positioned on the plug and pushed down over it with the yoke.

The two parts of the former are then clamped together to hold the plastic against the plug until it has cooled down. When the shape has 'set' it can be removed from the formers and the excess plastic cut away from the finished moulding.

Vacuum forming

Vacuum forming is quite similar to press moulding in many ways, but it can be used to produce deeper and more complex shapes. The process works by creating a vacuum underneath a softened thermoplastic sheet, allowing atmospheric pressure to push the plastic against the mould (plug).

Vacuum forming is widely used in manufacturing, with some of the best examples being items for packaging, where very thin, clear plastic can be formed into the shape of an object to protect it and allow it to be displayed. Many of the common thermoplastics can be used, but the two you are most likely to use in project work are ABS and HIPS.

Figure 7.22 Examples of vacuum formings

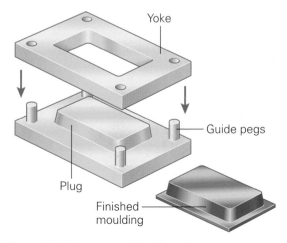

Figure 7.21 Press moulding

The design of the **mould** for a vacuum forming is very important, because as well as producing the shape required it must also allow it to be easily removed from the mould after forming. The sides of the mould need to be slightly tapered to give a draft angle and any corners should be radiused (rounded off). The rounding-off of corners is particularly important as it also reduces the risk of splitting the thin plastic as it is formed.

The mould should be made from a heat-resistant material and have a smooth surface, without any marks or defects that would show up on the vacuum forming. If a vacuum forming is to have a number of different depths or small recesses, it is often necessary to put vent holes in the mould. This is to ensure that all the air can be removed quickly, as any air trapped above the mould would prevent the softened plastic forming to the exact shape required.

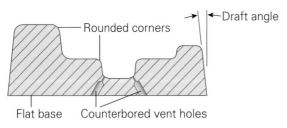

Figure 7.23 Vacuum-forming mould

Figure 7.24 Vacuum-forming machine

The vacuum-forming process is quite straightforward and often more than one item can be made at a time, depending on the size of the items and the size of the machine.

The mould to be used is placed on the platen in the bottom of the machine and then a sheet of thermoplastic is clamped firmly in place to give an airtight seal. The heating element is then moved into position above the plastic sheet and switched on.

When the plastic is flexible enough, the platen is raised to bring the mould into place and the vacuum is switched on. The softened plastic is forced onto the mould by atmospheric pressure, and when the shape is fully formed the heat is turned off, but the vacuum is left on to allow the shape to 'set'.

The 'blow' facility on the vacuum-forming machine can be used to help break the seal between the mould and the plastic after forming.

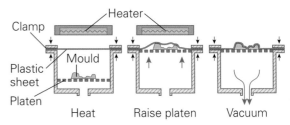

Figure 7.25 The vacuum-forming process

Blow moulding

Like vacuum forming, **blow moulding** uses air pressure to form softened thermoplastic sheet material, but in this case the air is compressed and blown directly against the plastic.

The simplest form of blow moulding is called free blowing. This is used to produce regular, dome-shaped objects, and the shape of the dome can be restricted to give a flat base for a bowl if required. The diameter of the dome or bowl produced is governed by the diameter of the hole in the clamping ring that holds the thermoplastic sheet in place for blowing.

For free blowing to be successful, the temperature of the plastic and the air pressure applied need to be carefully controlled, and it can be difficult to ensure that exactly the same size and shape are produced each time.

When larger numbers of items or more complex shapes are needed, the softened plastic is blown into a specially shaped mould. As with vacuum forming, the design of the mould is important and must include tapered sides and rounded corners to allow the finished moulding to be removed easily from the mould.

The most common application of blow moulding is in the manufacture of plastic bottles and other containers. In this application the blow moulding is carried out as part of a fully automated process that includes extrusion.

Blow moulding and vacuum forming are both processes that can readily be adapted to suit particular products, and in some cases they can also be combined. Large items made from fairly thick plastic sheet, such as acrylic baths, can be made by vacuum forming the shape in the normal way, but also using compressed air to force the plastic into the deep mould during forming.

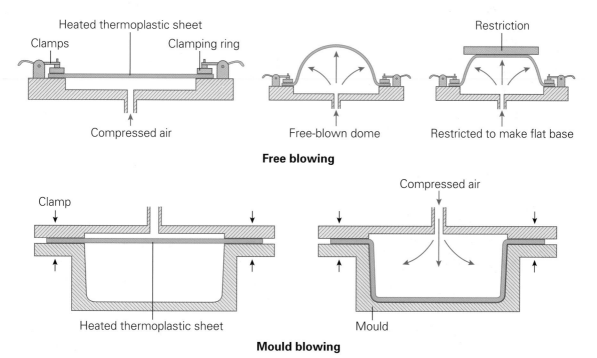

Figure 7.26 Blow-moulding

KEY TERMS

LINE BENDING – Bending plastic after softening a narrow strip.
PRESS MOULDING – Forming a hollow shape from a softened plastic sheet.
VACUUM FORMING – Producing thin hollow items over a shaped mould.
MOULD – Made to the shape required, to be used many times.
BLOW MOULDING – Using air pressure to blow softened plastic into shape.

ACTIVITY

The small storage box shown in Figure 7.27 has been made by vacuum forming ABS plastic. The box has sloping sides so that empty boxes can be stacked together for storage.

Figure 7.27 Plastic storage box

A lid is needed to fit into the top of the box to allow boxes to be stacked on top of each other when they are being used.

Design and make a mould for producing the box and the lid together on one sheet of plastic.

Draw a simple labelled sketch of the mould, showing the sizes for each part.

The size of the box can be made to suit the vacuum-forming machine you have in your school workshop. When you have vacuum formed the box and lid, check that the two parts fit together properly and comment on any problems you might find.

7.2 JOINING RESISTANT MATERIALS

EXAMINER'S TIPS

Examiners often ask questions about 'temporary' and 'permanent' methods of joining materials. Make sure you know the difference between these methods. Note that joining materials is also referred to as 'fabricating'.

Temporary methods of joining

Temporary means that the method of joining can be taken apart. These include the use of screws, nuts and bolts and KD fittings, which are known as pre-manufactured standard components. These are dealt with in Chapter 5.

Permanent methods of joining

Permanent means that once the materials have been joined they will remain joined forever. This includes the use of adhesives with wood, metal and plastics, riveting metal and heat processes used to join metal.

Adhesives

The main performance characteristics of a range of adhesives are described below.

PVA adhesive such as Evostik Resin 'W'

- Good general woodworking adhesive.
- Ready-mixed for ease of use.
- Water-resistant varieties available.
- Takes two to four hours to set and requires pressure through clamping.
- Few health and safety problems.

Contact adhesive such as Alpha/Dunlop Thixofix® or Evostik Time Bond

- Used to glue plastic laminate to manufactured boards (suitable for large areas).
- Apply evenly to both surfaces to be glued.
- Leave until 'touch-dry' (10–15 minutes).
- Position two surfaces accurately before applying final pressure to the two surfaces in contact.
- Precaution: because most of these adhesives set when the surfaces come into contact with each other, accurate positioning is essential.

Synthetic resin adhesive such as Cascamite

- Excellent woodworking adhesive, especially designed for boat building or any work in contact with water.
- White glue powder mixed with water to a creamy consistency.
- When mixed must be used within 30 minutes; wasteful if not used up.
- Apply to joints and cramp together under pressure and allow six hours to set.

Epoxy resin adhesive such as Araldite™

- Used to glue together a variety of materials: wood, metal, some plastics, ceramics and glass.
- Two parts in two tubes: resin (glue) and hardener (catalyst).
- Two parts mixed in equal amounts.
- Pressure through clamping or weights is essential.
- Quick-drying varieties will set in three to four hours. Heat makes the drying process quicker.

Polystyrene cement

- Used to join rigid polystyrene such as that used on model kits.
- Dries quickly and gives a clear joint.
- Can be messy, but surplus cement can be removed with acetone.

Tensol cement

- Used to join acrylic.
- Ready-for-use, solvent-based cement.
- Sets quickly.
- Surrounding area of joint should be masked off to avoid cement marking surface.
- Pressure is required while setting takes place.
- Precautions: good ventilation is essential when using Tensol; avoid contact with skin.

Nails

Nails alone do not provide a permanent joint. It is the adhesive used with the nail that provides permanence. The use of nails to provide a strong wood joint is dealt with in Chapter 5.

Joints in wood

Joints used in the construction of wooden products can be broadly classified into three groups: carcass or box construction, stool construction and frame construction.

Carcass or box construction

Although they are called different names, the cabinet and box are basically the same product using the same constructions.

Joints that could be used at the corners include comb (finger), butt, dowel, mitre and half-lap.

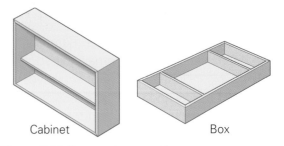

Cabinet   Box

Figure 7.28 Carcass construction

Shelves and partitions can be fitted using housing joints. It is not always necessary to reinforce the butt joint as long as it is nailed and glued. The number of dowels needed can also be reduced, depending on the size and purpose of the carcass. The purpose of the veneer keys is to reinforce the mitre joint. Without this strengthening the joint would be quite weak. Housing joints are used to fit shelves and partitions. The stopped housing

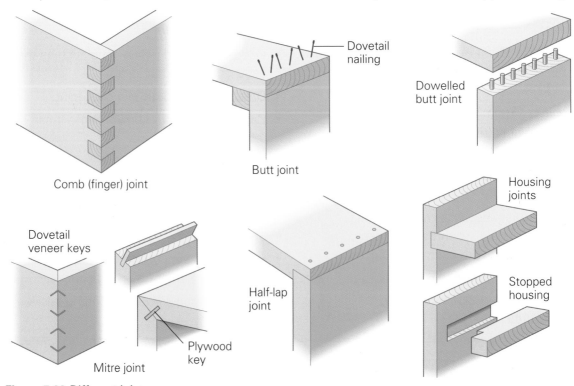

Comb (finger) joint

Butt joint

Dovetail nailing

Dowelled butt joint

Dovetail veneer keys

Mitre joint

Plywood key

Half-lap joint

Housing joints

Stopped housing

Figure 7.29 Different joints

looks better than the through housing since you cannot see the bottom of the housing on the front edge.

Stool construction

Stool construction is used when making small tables or stools and involves the joining of rails to legs. Joints that could be used include dowel, bridle, and mortise and tenon. Notice how when the rails enter the leg, the ends of the tenons have to be mitred at 45 degrees so that both tenons fit properly.

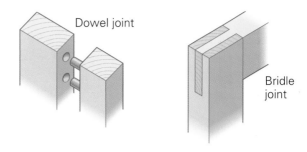

Dowel joint

Bridle joint

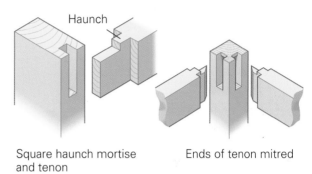

Haunch

Square haunch mortise and tenon

Ends of tenon mitred

Figure 7.31 Different joints

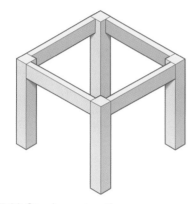

Figure 7.30 Stool construction

Frame construction

Frame construction is used to make doors with panels inserted or with manufactured board covering the frame. Joints that could be used at the corners include butt, corner halving, mitre, dowel, mortise and tenon, and bridle. The butt joint can be strengthened with corner pieces or a fastener. The flush door gets its strength not from the butt joint, but from the nails and adhesive used to fix the door panel to the frame. The cross-halving joint is used to allow both cross rails to 'cross' each other inside the frame. You can see that the dowel, mortise and tenon and bridle joints used in stool construction could also be used in frame construction.

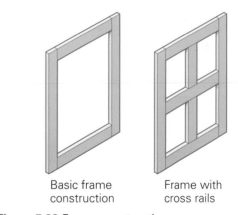

Basic frame construction

Frame with cross rails

Figure 7.32 Frame construction

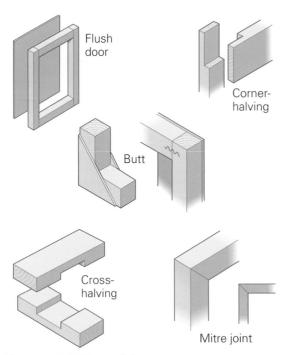

Figure 7.33 **Different joints**

Riveting

Rivets are a quick way of joining metal sheets and thin metal. You do not need to know how to rivet, but be aware of different types and where they are used.

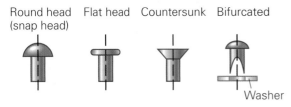

Figure 7.34 **Types of rivet**

Round or snap-head rivets are used where a countersunk or flush finish is not needed.

Countersunk head rivets are the most commonly used and provide a flush surface.

Flat-head or tinmans rivets are used in thin material where a countersunk is not possible.

Bifurcated rivets are used to join soft materials such as leather and plastics.

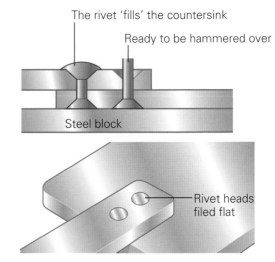

Figure 7.35 **The riveting process**

When using countersunk head rivets to join thin metal, the rivet is hammered over to fill the countersink. The surplus metal is then filed off to produce a flush finish.

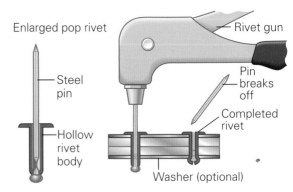

Figure 7.36 **Pop riveting**

Pop riveting was developed for use in the construction of aircraft. Pop riveting is used to fasten thin sheet metal and other materials. Washers can be used so that soft materials can be fastened. Because the rivets used in the pop rivet gun are hollow, they are not as strong as solid rivets.

Holes are first drilled through the pieces to be joined. The hollow rivet is mounted on a head pin, which is pushed into the rivet gun. The rivet is pushed into the pre-drilled holes and the gun is squeezed. This has the effect of pulling the pin through and expanding the rivet head. When the correct pressure is reached, the pin breaks off, leaving the formed rivet with the pin head in it.

Heat processes to join metal

Soldering makes a permanent joint between metals by melting an alloy, with a lower melting point than the metal being joined, between the metals. Soft soldering, hard soldering and brazing are all types of soldering.

Preparation is essential for successful soldering:

1. The area of the joint must be cleaned using a file, emery cloth or steel wool. Solder will only stick to clean metal.

2. A flux is applied. The purpose of the flux is to keep the surfaces clean and provide oxidisation when the heat is applied. In addition, the flux helps the solder flow into the joint. There are different types of flux for different situations.

Soft soldering

Soft solder is an alloy of lead and tin in varying amounts. Common uses for soft soldering include joining copper water pipes and also to solder electrical/electronic connections. Soft soldering can be carried out using a brazing torch or soldering iron because of the low melting point of the solder.

Hard soldering

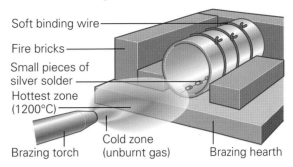

Figure 7.37 Hard soldering process

Hard soldering is also known as silver soldering because the solder is an alloy of silver, copper and zinc. The joint needs to be close-fitting and clean. Several small pieces of silver solder are cut from a strip and placed on the joint. The brazing torch is used to heat the metal gently at first, before a small hot flame is used to heat the metal to dull red. At this stage the solder will run along the joint.

Brazing

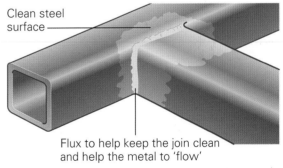

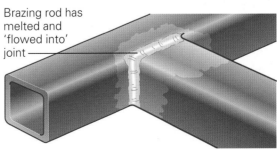

Figure 7.38 Brazing two pieces of square steel tube

Brazing is used to join steel together by melting brazing rod between the two pieces of metal to be joined. Preparation is similar to that of soft and hard soldering. The steel is heated until red-hot and the brazing rod is placed against the join. The brazing rod melts and flows along the join. The steel is then allowed to cool without quenching.

Welding

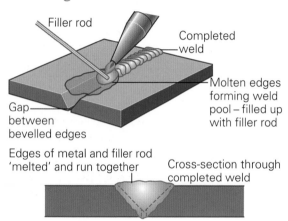

Figure 7.39 Oxyacetylene welding

Two common forms of welding are oxyacetylene and electric arc. Welding is done by applying extreme heat to the two surfaces to be joined.

The oxyacetylene method uses a mixture of the two gases to produce 3500°C heat. The heat melts the two surfaces, causing a gap to develop. This gap is filled by applying a filler rod that melts into the joint and fuses the surfaces together.

The electric-arc method uses a flux-coated filler rod that acts as an electrode. Heat is achieved by sending a low-voltage, high electrical current between the filler rod and the metals to be joined.

QUESTIONS

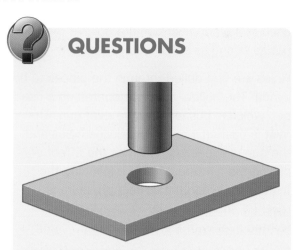

Figure 7.40 Rod and base to be joined

The two components shown in Figure 7.40 could be made from wood, metal or plastics.

- Name a suitable waterproof adhesive that could be used to glue the pieces of wood together.
- Name a solvent used to glue the acrylic plastic together.
- Name a method of joining the pieces of mild steel together permanently.
- Name a method of joining the pieces of mild steel together temporarily.

KEY TERMS

FABRICATING – Refers to the way materials are joined together.
SOLDERING – A method of making a permanent joint between metals by melting an alloy between them that has a lower melting point than the metals being joined.

7.3 FINISHING PROCESSES APPLIED TO RESISTANT MATERIALS

Metal finishes

Primers and paints

When painting metal it is important to apply at least three coats: primer, undercoat and top coat.

The primer is applied to the bare metal to help the undercoat and top-coat paints to adhere to the metal. An undercoat is applied as the preparation for the final coat. An oil-based gloss finish would be applied finally.

There are traditional oil-based primers and undercoats, but acrylic paints can be used as a single primer and undercoat. The advantage of acrylic paint is that it dries quicker, allowing you to recoat sooner.

Hammerite™ is a 'one-coat' paint, available in a smooth or hammered finish, that gives a quick-drying protective finish for ferrous metals, without the need for a primer or undercoat.

Electroplating

This process enables metals to be protected and their appearance improved by coating their surface with a thin film of metal. The thin film is fused electrically onto the surface. The coating should be less 'reactive' and resistant to chemical attack. Chromium plating is often used to coat car parts, sink and bath taps and cycle parts.

Anodising

Anodising is a process applied to aluminium. The process is similar to electroplating, except that no additional metal is used. Aluminium develops a thin film of oxide that forms a protective layer. This layer can be thickened by anodising. Coloured dyes are often added to provide an attractive metallic surface finish.

Dip-coating

Products that are dip-coated include refrigerator shelves, freezer baskets and tool handles for electrical pliers.

Dip-coating can be carried out in school workshops using polythene in powder form. Polythene is tough and durable. The process is carried out by heating in an oven to 180°C the metal to be coated. The metal is then plunged into a tank of 'fluidised' polythene powder for a few seconds. Fluidisation involves blowing air through the powder in a small tank to make the powder behave like liquid. This way the coating will be applied more evenly to the workpiece. The workpiece is then reheated in an oven to produce a smooth, even finish. Finally, it is left to cool.

Polishing

Items of jewellery made from non-ferrous metals, such as copper, brass, gold and silver, are often polished to allow their natural colour to show through. Depending on the size and shape of the jewellery, polishing can be carried out by hand, using metal polish, or by means of a polishing mop fitted onto the wheel of a buffing machine. Polishing compound is applied to the mop and the workpiece held against the mop as it rotates. A high-quality polished finish can be achieved, but to prevent the polished surface becoming tarnished, a clear lacquer may be applied by means of a brush or spray.

▶ Wood finishes

Varnishes

Polyurethane varnishes give a clear, tough and hard-wearing finish. They provide a plastic coating without actually penetrating the surface of the wood. They are available in matt, satin and gloss finishes. There are coloured varnishes that provide the colour and tough finish in one coat.

Traditional polyurethane varnishes have long drying times, up to eight hours. Recent developments, including quick-drying, water-based polymer varnishes, now mean that you can apply a varnish that dries in 20 minutes and can be recoated in one hour. To achieve a high-quality finish, up to six coats of polyurethane varnish may be applied. A very fine grade of glasspaper should be used to rub down between each coat of varnish.

Marine or 'yacht' varnish has a specific use for products used in water, such as boats.

Primers and paints

The principles of painting wood are the same as those for metal: primer to seal the wood, followed by an undercoat and then a final gloss coat.

Paint is available in many forms. Emulsion paints are suitable for covering large areas such as walls because they are relatively inexpensive and can be applied quickly with a large brush or roller. They are water-based and not very durable. Oil-based paints, including non-drip types, are tough, hard-wearing and weatherproof. Acrylic paints are quick-drying and can be applied straight onto wood or even on top of varnish.

Stains

Stains do not actually protect the wood. Their primary use is to show off the grain and make it look like a different and sometimes more expensive wood; for example, there are light oak and dark oak stains. Bright-coloured stains are sometimes used on children's toys. Stains are not easy to apply and they can be difficult to match, so it is advisable to test them on scrap wood first.

Polishes

There are numerous different clear liquid polishes that can be applied to wood. Clear polish allows the beauty of the wood grain to show through. French polish is a mixture of methylated spirits and shellac and is applied by a cloth rubber (a wad of cotton wool wrapped inside a piece of cloth). There are other similar polishes, including white and button. These polishes are often used to seal the grain before finishing with a wax polish. The important part of the process is to build up each of the layers gradually, making sure that each coat is sanded down before the next one is applied.

Oils

Oils give a natural finish as they help prevent wood from drying out and they replace the wood's natural oil. Teak oil can be applied to teak and iroko, which are oily woods. Olive oil can be applied to kitchenware that will come into contact with food as it is colourless and odourless. Danish oil is made mainly from linseed oil and is excellent for interior and exterior furniture.

Wax

Wax polish can be applied on top of bare wood or wood sealed with French polish. Beeswax is the traditional wax and may be applied to bare wood. The dull gloss shine would result after numerous applications. Silicone wax gives greater protection where hot drinks may be placed.

Preservatives

Whereas varnishes provide protection by adding a plastic coating on top of the surface of the wood, preservatives penetrate deeply into the wood. Wood used outdoors can be affected by fungus, insects or weather. Preservatives are widely available in a variety of colours and are a big improvement on the traditional creosote that was the most common preservative used on sheds and fencing.

EXAMINER'S TIP

When examination questions ask you to name a suitable finish, your answer needs to be precise. With so many different finishes on the market, you can understand why examiners are unlikely to reward vague answers such as 'paint' or 'varnish'.

▶ Plastics: self-finishing and polishing

Most project work in school involves the use of acrylic sheet. The surface of acrylic plastic is highly polished and shiny. To maintain this finish it is important to keep the backing paper or plastic film on the surface when working the material. The edges of the plastic become rough and scratched when sawn, sanded or filed. To produce the same quality of finish to the edges as the surface, the following processes should be carried out:

- Draw-filing or the use of a scraper will remove deep scratches. (Scrapers can be made from old hacksaw blades.)
- Rub the edges on a sheet of silicon carbide (wet and dry) paper fastened to a board or wrap the paper around a cork block to keep the edges square. Use a medium/coarse grit 150.
- Repeat the process, using a finer grit 400.
- Apply an appropriate polishing compound, such as Vonax®, to a soft calico mop and apply the edge of the plastic to it to produce a high-quality finish. It is essential to use the correct mop and polishing compound and to apply the correct pressure. Too hard a mop or too much pressure will heat the plastic and actually melt the edge you want to appear highly polished.

▶ Surface preparation for the application of a finish

Preparing metal

There are different processes for different metals requiring different finishes. If a bright finish is required for steel, there are a number of important processes to be carried out. It may need to be draw-filed along its length in one direction before it is cleaned with various grades of emery cloth. The grades should vary from coarse to fine, with each grade resulting in finer scratches that will become so fine as to be virtually invisible.

Alternatively, if the steel is to be painted, less attention needs to be placed on the quality of finish as it will be covered. The surface will need to be degreased before applying the paint. This would be done using paraffin or white spirit.

Copper and brass would be pickled in a bath of dilute sulphuric acid to degrease and remove oxides. The metal would be cleaned using pumice powder applied with a damp cloth, then rinsed in water to remove all traces of acid.

Preparing wood

Wood can be planed using a finely set smoothing plane. A cabinet scraper will remove scratches and tears in wood with cross or interlocking grain. Various grades of glasspaper should be used. Wrap the glasspaper around a cork block so that even pressure can be applied to the wood, and always use the glasspaper along the grain. If you go across the grain, the glasspaper will leave scratches.

Start with a medium/fine grade of glasspaper such as F2, and work down to a finer grade 1. It is good practice to wipe off the dust with a damp cloth between applications. On large areas an orbital or belt sander can be used. You will need to take care with a belt sander as they tend to be fierce and need more control. You will still need to work through the different grades of glasspaper when using a machine sander.

▶ Reasons for the use of specific finishes in particular applications

There are three reasons for finishing a product:

- to protect the wood from weathering and the risk of decay
- to protect the wood from minor scratches and abrasions
- to improve the appearance of the surface of the product.

Specific finishes are applied to:

- seal the surface of wood or metal to provide a base for further coats of paint
- insulate from electricity – for example, the handle of electrician's pliers could be plastic-coated
- protect from spillage of liquids or heat from drinks – for example, using polyurethane varnish on the top of a coffee table
- protect from the weather – for example, using wood preservative on outdoor furniture
- make a cheaper wood appear as a more expensive one – for example, using teak wood stain on birch wood
- provide a base metal with protection and a more attractive appearance – for example, electroplating nickel jewellery with silver
- replace natural oils in wood – for example, using olive oil on a cheeseboard
- enhance and improve the appearance – for example, waxing a mahogany cabinet
- prevent tarnishing – for example, using lacquer on copper jewellery
- prevent rusting – for example, galvanising steel.

▶ Application of finishes by means of brush or spray

The main advantages of using a brush are that it is quick and needs no special equipment.

The main advantages of spraying are that it provides a more consistent and even finish.

When using a brush it is important that it is clean before you start, that your brushstrokes are in the same direction and that you clean the brush immediately after use. Oil-based paints and varnishes should be cleaned with white spirit, but acrylic-based paints and emulsions can be cleaned in soap and water.

It is not easy to achieve a high-quality spray finish. Aerosol cans of spray paint are excellent for small jobs, but larger areas may need a spray gun used with a small compressor. Health and safety rules insist on spraying being carried out in a well-ventilated area and the wearing of a breathing mask.

QUESTIONS

1. Name a different abrasive paper used when preparing or finishing wood, metal and plastics.

2. Name a suitable finish or finishing process for each of the products shown below.

Figure 7.41 Pair of pliers

Figure 7.42 Bath taps

Figure 7.43 Copper bracelet

Figure 7.44 Outdoor table and chairs

Figure 7.45 Wooden cutting board

ICT, CAD AND CAM

By the end of this chapter you should have developed a knowledge and understanding of:

- the use of CAD packages in school
- on-screen modelling
- appropriate use of text, database and graphics software
- the storage and sharing of data electronically
- practical applications of CAD/CAM
- CNC (computer numerical control) machines.

This chapter is concerned with the use of computers to help you when you are involved in the practical activities of designing and making. It is to do with designing, drawing, word processing, modelling and making. Much of the chapter will concentrate on the two important areas of CAD (computer-aided design) and CAM (computer-aided manufacture). It will look at software that enables you to design in 2D and 3D, and machines that can transfer your designs into 3D working products. Although this is important to your practical work and you will be expected to use CAD/CAM in Units 2 and 4, examiners may also ask questions about CAD/CAM in the written papers, so you need to know what the benefits of using CAD/CAM are.

8.1 USE OF CAD PACKAGES IN SCHOOL

Two-dimensional CAD software packages such as Techsoft 2D Design V2 are straightforward to use and offer many features that allow you to produce different types of design drawings. Not only can you draw, design and model on screen, but with your computer linked to a compatible machine, you can actually see your product made by the machine.

- You can produce accurate, fully dimensioned 'technical drawings'.

- You can create manufacturing drawings that can then be outputted to a variety of CAM devices such as vinyl cutters, plotter/engravers, millers, routers and laser cutters.

- You can undertake graphic design activity, allowing you to combine vector graphics, text, bitmap images, photographs and Clip Art to create and manipulate images for items such as logos, menus, point-of-sale display and product packaging.

Three-dimensional CAD packages such as SolidWorks® and Prodesktop® give you the opportunity to develop working drawings that include both 2D and 3D images of your design ideas. These can be analysed and amended on screen. In addition, you can generate outstanding, professional presentation drawings.

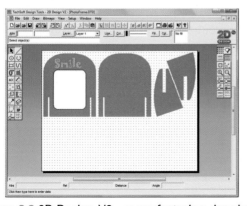

Figure 8.1 Technical drawing produced using 2D Design V2

Figure 8.2 2D Design V2 – manufacturing drawings for photo frame and final product

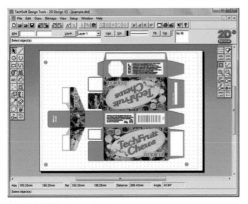

Figure 8.3 Working drawings

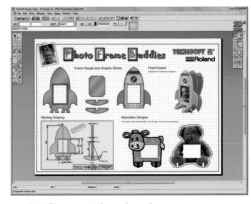

Figure 8.4 Presentation drawing

8.2 ON-SCREEN MODELLING AND IMAGE MANIPULATION

Most software allows you to cleverly control the drawings you produce on screen. Features include the ability to zoom in on drawings or to rotate in order to view the drawing from all angles. The 2D Design program gives you the opportunity to convert drawings from bitmap images such as JPEG files into vector paths. This means that drawings you have made by hand or scanned can be converted on screen. This, in turn, means that they could provide the paths to be cut or engraved by machines connected to the computer. Drawings can be rendered to produce photorealistic images. Software enables you to determine the lighting effects, the material and texture and even background scenery. Some software includes automated assembly, using nuts, bolts, screws and other components. Animation means that it is possible to see an accurate moving image of a design.

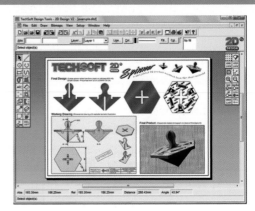

Figure 8.5 Figure spinner

On a single sheet it is possible to produce working drawings, a presentation drawing and manufacturing drawings. It is vital that you invest a portion of your time trying out some of the features that the software offers.

8.3 TEXT, DATABASE AND GRAPHICS SOFTWARE

Word-processing software

Word-processing, or text, software was originally designed just to produce text documents, but many of the programs available now are very versatile and can be used in a number of ways. The most commonly used word-processing program is Microsoft® Word. This is not only used to produce text, but also allows tables and simple drawings to be created, and material to be pasted in from other programs to add to and illustrate a document. One really useful feature of word-processing programs is the fact that they offer spelling and grammar checks and provide on-screen reminders of when these checks are needed.

Most word-processing packages come with a selection of Clip Art, which is the name given to files of pre-prepared pictures that can be used in the text. To find a Clip Art picture, click on the Insert menu and select Picture and then Clip Art. When you have found a suitable picture, click on it to insert it into your document and then move, enlarge or reduce it by using the mouse.

Database software

Databases are used to store and process information, and each piece of data is referred to as an entry on the database. A telephone directory is an example of a database, but computerised databases are much more useful as they can be used to access information very quickly. As well as storing a lot of information, you can also use the database to add to, delete or modify the information when required, without affecting the rest of the entries.

Most computerised databases have Sort and Filter functions to allow you to rearrange the information into different orders or groups. The example shown in Figure 8.7 is a database with details of the tools needed in a school workshop. The Sort function could be used to rearrange the tools on the database into alphabetical order, and the Filter function could give a list of the tools in a particular cupboard number for stock checking.

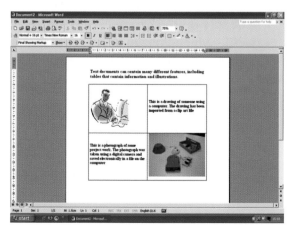

Figure 8.6 An illustrated text document

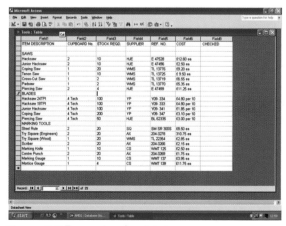

Figure 8.7 Example of a database

▶ Spreadsheet software

Spreadsheets are quite similar to databases because they look like tables of information, but they are able to perform other functions in addition to storing and sorting information. A spreadsheet allows you to enter text and numbers into a table and then carry out calculations on them. They can be used to help calculate the total cost of a project by entering details of all the things needed and how much each one costs.

One of the most common programs used for spreadsheets is Microsoft Excel®, which also allows charts to be produced to present the data on the spreadsheet graphically. Once the spreadsheet has been produced, a Chart Wizard is used to draw whichever type of chart is needed to display the information. Different types of charts can be produced, and you can use this function to help present the results of surveys you might do in your project work.

In the example shown in Figure 8.8, a group of people have been asked to say what their favourite holiday destination is. The results of the survey have been put into a spreadsheet

and the Chart Wizard function has then been used to present the information in a pie chart.

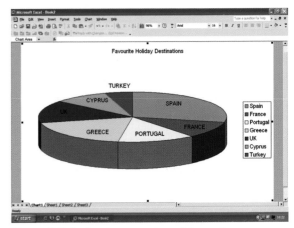

Figure 8.9 A pie chart produced from the spreadsheet

ACTIVITY

1. Carry out a simple survey in your group to find out the group members' favourite colour or type of music.

2. Enter the results of your survey into a spreadsheet and produce a chart to present the results graphically.

3. Try out the different types of charts available on the Chart Wizard and decide which you think presents the information in the clearest form.

4. When you have decided on the type of chart to use, produce a fully labelled version and keep a copy of the spreadsheet and the chart in your folder.

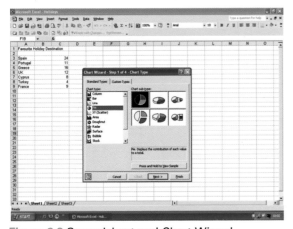

Figure 8.8 Spreadsheet and Chart Wizard

Spreadsheets are used a lot by businesses to help calculate their costs and profits. Relevant data is usually transferred from a database to produce a spreadsheet for a particular purpose, and the spreadsheet software then allows the user to see what effects any changes to the data would have. They could calculate how much an increase in the cost of one part would reduce the amount of profit made, or what could be saved by leaving out one part, such as using only three screws instead of four for assembling a product.

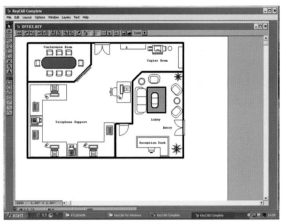

Figure 8.10 A simple 2D CAD drawing

Graphics software

Graphics software packages come in many forms, ranging from simple collections of Clip Art to complex packages that allow 3D modelling and animation to be carried out. The software that you use at school or college will depend on what is available on the network, but many of the packages can be used on your home PC or laptop.

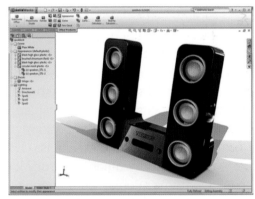

Figure 8.11 3D CAD drawings

When using CAD packages to produce drawings, it is best to choose the program that is most suitable for what you want to draw. Do not be tempted to use a powerful 3D CAD package when the drawing you want to produce can be drawn more easily and quickly on an alternative program, such as Techsoft 2D Design. All that really matters is that the drawing you produce is clear and shows what you want it to show.

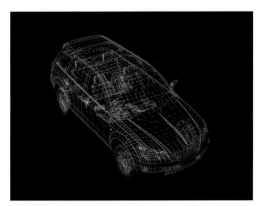

Figure 8.12 3D CAD of car

KEY TERMS

CLIP ART – Files of ready-prepared drawings.

DATABASE – A document for storing and processing information (data).

SPREADSHEET – Text and numbers contained in a table allowing calculations to be carried out.

WIZARD – Part of a program that helps perform a particular function.

GRAPHICS SOFTWARE – Computer programs to produce drawings.

8.4 STORING AND SHARING DATA

KEY POINT

- As the amount of data produced and used on computers increases, so the need for this data to be stored in large amounts becomes more important. The size of any storage device is referred to by how much **memory** it has, and items such as photographs from digital cameras and drawings from CAD packages take up a lot of memory, particularly when compared with simple text documents. Most data is normally stored on the **hard drive** of a PC or the **server** of a network, but with the increasing use of laptops, notebooks and PDAs (personal digital assistants), more portable storage devices have been developed to allow important files to be carried around and shared between individual machines.

The amount of memory needed is determined by the file size, measured in bytes and usually expressed as a number of kilobytes or megabytes.

- 1 kilobyte (KB) = 1000 bytes
- 1 megabyte (MB) = 1 million bytes
- 1 gigabyte (GB) = 1000 million bytes
- 1 terabyte (TB) = 1 million million bytes

Some examples of typical file sizes are:

- a page of text – 30 KB
- a simple CAD drawing – 200 KB
- a high-resolution photograph – 20 MB.

Some computers still have the facility to use a floppy disk, which normally has a capacity of 1.44 MB, meaning that it could store about seven CAD drawings, but would not be big enough for even one high-resolution photograph. Although these floppy disks are no longer used, external floppy disk drives are available to connect to the computer through a **USB** port, allowing the old disks to be used to transfer the files to another device.

Floppy disks were replaced some time ago by the **CD-ROM**, which has a capacity of 700 MB and could therefore store over 30 high-resolution photographs. More recently, DVDs were introduced, and although these are normally associated with films, they can also be used in the same way as CDs, but are capable of storing much more data.

Memory sticks are very widely used to store data and their capacity is increasing all the time. These devices are also referred to as pen drives and flash drives, and capacities of 8 GB and more are not uncommon. Not only are these devices small and convenient to carry around, but files can easily be deleted from them, unlike the CD-ROM with its read-only memory.

External hard drives can be connected through a USB port to increase the memory and improve the speed of a computer, and these are now being made so much smaller in physical size that they are easily carried in a pocket. The trend is to increase the capacity and reduce the size of storage devices so that more and more information can be conveniently stored and carried around.

Data that is stored electronically is very easy to share with other people in a number of ways, and one of the most widely used methods is the internet. Information can be put onto a website so that it can be downloaded by anyone, or it can be sent electronically to individuals as attachments to emails. Because storage devices are physically small but able to hold large amounts of data, the devices themselves can be sent by secure delivery methods to prevent important data being accessed illegally.

Figure 8.13 Memory sticks and external hard drive

KEY TERMS

USB – Universal serial bus, used to connect external devices to the computer.
CD-ROM – A compact disk storage device with read-only memory.
MEMORY STICK (PEN DRIVE) – Storage device connected to a computer through a USB port.
EXTERNAL HARD DRIVE – Portable storage device with large capacity.

8.5 APPLICATIONS OF CAD/CAM

Designing and making models and prototypes

On-screen models can help you to visualise what the final product will look like. Prototype models can be made by downloading data from your computer images to a machine that can reproduce the design exactly.

Rapid prototyping is the manufacture of a

replica model of a final product, the only difference being the material in which the model is made. The term 'rapid' describes the speed with which the model is manufactured, compared with the final actual product made from resistant materials.

Commercial rapid prototyping involves the building up of layers of material to achieve the shape, but it is possible to use machines in school that use a milling cutter to remove material from a block to achieve the finished shape of a product.

Figure 8.14 On-screen modelling

Figure 8.15 Prototype model

EXAMINER'S TIPS

CAM can help you to achieve a high-quality product. Projects where CAM is used to complete part of the product are the best as far as assessment of your work is concerned in Units 2 and 4. This is because it is vital that you are able to demonstrate a range of skills, other than CAM, in the products you make. A project to design and make an educational toy can involve the design and manufacture of the vinyl letters to go on the blocks.

Figure 8.16 Letter blocks

This could be done by designing the letters on screen. You could try different types of font, different sizes and colours to match the vinyl you will make them from. Then download the design data from your computer to a machine such as a Roland CAMM1 vinyl cutter. This would produce excellent letters, which could then be peeled off a backing sheet and stuck onto the wooden blocks.

Another educational toy could be manufactured totally using CAD/CAM.

Figure 8.17 Roland CAMM 1 GX24

Figure 8.20 Roland RotoCAMM MDX40

Figure 8.18 Alphabet letters

Having designed the letters on screen, these could be made using either a laser cutter or a miller/router.

Figure 8.19 Laser CAMM A2

Benefits of CAD/CAM

EXAMINER'S TIPS

When asked an examination question about the benefits of CAD/CAM, many students simply state 'quicker', 'faster', 'accurate' and receive no marks. Try to write a sentence that describes clearly a specific benefit, as in the examples below.

CAD:

- Computers can be used to make changes to a design and edit it without having to redraw it.
- Computers can be used to produce very accurate drawings and dimensions of exactly what is drawn.
- Computers can produce photorealistic models without having to make them.
- Computers can show or simulate how a product will behave without having to undertake expensive testing.

CAM:

- Computers do not make mistakes if programmed properly.
- Computers give reliable and consistently high standards of manufacture.
- Computers achieve quicker production times. Complex shapes and designs can be created easily.

KEY POINT

- CAD/CAM refers to the use of computer software to help in the designing and making of a product. A program with details of the design produced by CAD is transferred to a CAM machine for the product to be made. The CAM element of CAD/CAM can relate to the production of a single prototype or to the quantity manufacture of a final product.

▶ One-off and quantity production

The designing and modelling of a product is done as a 'one-off' production operation (see Chapter 4) and any changes to the design that are required are made while the final prototype is developed. Once the software program has been finalised, it can then be used to make the product in whatever quantity is needed. The CAM machines that you use in school are really only designed to make products on a one-off basis, but small quantities of identical products (batches) can be produced by using specially made **fixtures** to position the work on the machines.

When producing very large quantities of products on an industrial scale, automated systems are used for positioning and clamping work on machines so that they can work more quickly. Machines are also often linked together as part of a completely automatic production line (see Chapter 4).

KEY TERMS

RAPID PROTOTYPING – The manufacture of a replica model of a final product.
FIXTURE – A specially made device for holding parts to be machined. It is 'fixed' onto the machine to hold the part securely.

8.6 COMPUTER NUMERICAL CONTROL (CNC) MACHINES

KEY POINT

- Any machine that is controlled by a computer is a **CNC** machine because all computer control is numerical.

To make a part on a CNC machine, a program is needed to control the movement of the cutting tool in relation to the material being cut. The program is usually imported direct from a suitable CAD package as part of the whole CAD/CAM process.

In the case of a CNC lathe, the program controls the movement of the cutting tools, but on a CNC router or milling machine the program controls the movement of the machine table as well as the vertical movement of the cutting tool. When a number of different cutting tools are needed to complete the part, the program makes sure that the correct tool is selected and positioned for each operation.

Laser cutting machines do not have 'tools' in the usual sense of the word, but control of the machine is the same as for a CNC router or milling machine, with the movement of the laser beam being computer controlled (see Chapter 4).

Figure 8.23 Parts made by CNC machining

CNC machines that are used in industry are much larger and more powerful than the ones you may see in school. CNC lathes, laser cutters, routers and milling machines are all widely used, and machines are also made to be able to carry out many different processes. A typical CNC **machining centre** used in a factory will be able to carry out turning, drilling, milling and boring, and would have tool storage for all the necessary tools to carry out these operations, and a turret for changing the tools when necessary.

Figure 8.21 CNC lathe milling machine for training use

Figure 8.22 Milling machine for training use

Figure 8.24 Industrial CNC machine

KEY TERMS

CNC (COMPUTER NUMERICAL CONTROL) – Controlled by computer.
MACHINING CENTRE – A machine that can carry out different operations.

CHAPTER 9

UNIT 1: THE EXAMINATION PAPER

By the end of this chapter you should have developed a knowledge and understanding of:

- the structure of the exam paper
- effective examination technique
- the 'command' words used in the exam papers.

Unit 1 is a two-hour examination and it is worth 40 per cent of your GCSE marks. It consists of eight questions and is externally marked. The exam can be sat in the summer of the first or second year of the course.

The format of the paper is designed to be clear and straightforward. The headings for each question will remain the same each year and are reflected in the chapters in this book. This will allow you to know what information and knowledge to learn for each question on the paper.

The paper is divided into two sections, A and B. Each section is worth 20 per cent of the GCSE and each should take you one hour to complete. Each section is worth 60 marks, giving a total of 120 marks for the paper.

Each question is designed to start off easy and become progressively more difficult; this will allow everyone to gain at least some marks in each question.

▶ Section A

Section A consists of four questions based on the design of products, reflecting the wider aspects of sustainability and human use.

Question 3 asks you to produce an extended piece of writing that will assess the 'quality of written communication'. This is based on your study of two famous designers; your teacher will tell you the names of the

Question 1		Product analysis	15 marks
Question 2		General issues of D&T	10 marks
Question 3		Designers	10 marks
Question 4		Designing and the design process	25 marks
Total			60 marks

Table 9.1 Section A

designers to study. To achieve good marks on this question it is important that you talk about the work and inspiration of the designer and not where they were born, etc.

Part of Question 4 will require you to produce a solution to a design question. This question will assess your quality of communication and presentation.

▶ Section B

Section B consists of four questions based on the technical aspects of the processes, systems, materials, tools and equipment used in resistant materials.

▶ What equipment will I need for the examination?

Unit 1 is a very important part of the course and you need to be fully prepared for sitting the examination. It is recommended you have the following equipment when tackling the examination:

- black pen
- pencil, ruler, eraser and compass
- selection of coloured pencils.

Question 5		Commercial manufacturing processes	10 marks
Question 6		Materials and components	15 marks
Question 7		Tools, equipment and making	20 marks
Question 8		ICT, CAD/CAM, systems and processes	15 marks
TOTAL			60 marks

Table 9.2 Section B

How can I achieve my best in the Unit 4 examination?

Think of Design and Technology: Resistant Materials as the practical experiences of designing and making. You will have spent many hours working with materials, tools, equipment, machines and computers, and this practical experience is the most effective way of learning about the subject. However, you need to support these activities with a range of resources, including notes, handouts, research, tests and homework. You will have been given a folder/book for the whole course to keep this work safe. Do try to keep your work in an organised way so that you can use it for revision. Use section dividers and use the chapters from this book as a guideline.

Examination success depends on a variety of factors, including:

- revision – this is very important
- exam practice – take every opportunity to practise examination papers, as this will develop your examination technique
- understanding the 'command' words that are used in examination papers.

The exam questions require you to answer in a variety of ways: one-word answers, short sentences, completing tables, using sketches and notes and giving detailed explanations.

Whichever type of answer is required, you need to look carefully at the number of marks available, as this reflects the amount of time or detail expected of you for a good answer. The number of marks will be shown in brackets [ ] at the end of each question or part of a question. You should not spend too much time on questions that carry one or two marks, or provide superficial answers to questions that carry four or five marks.

You need to:

- be really familiar with the style, layout and requirements of the papers; you should have worked on past papers
- make your thinking totally clear, and ensure that nothing is left open to interpretation by the examiner
- read through each question carefully before you start to answer; you must be clear about what the question is asking you to do and how you are to answer
- apply specific design and technology knowledge rather than general knowledge, and try to use technical terminology accurately.

Examiners will not give any marks to answers such as 'strong', 'cheap', 'quick' or 'easy'. On their own these terms are meaningless. To gain a mark they need to be justified. For example, a joint could be 'strong' enough to take the weight of the tabletop; a softwood could be relatively 'cheap' when compared with hardwoods; vacuum forming is a 'quick' process once the moulds have been manufactured; using CAD is 'easy' only after the user has learnt the program.

Command words

'State ...', 'Name ...', 'Give ...'

These types of questions require you to give the specific name of, for example, a tool, process, construction or material. Normally, a one- or two-word answer will be sufficient. These types of question are worth one mark.

Example questions:

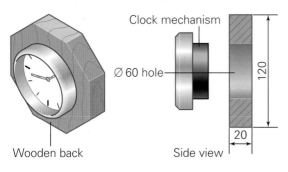

Figure 9.1

1. Figure 9.1 shows a clock that will be hung on a wall. The clock has a mechanism that fits into a hole in the wooden back.

(a) State *one* safety precaution you would take when using a sanding machine. [1]

(b) Name a suitable hardwood for the wooden back. [1]

(c) Give a reason for your choice of hardwood. [1]

'Describe ...', 'Explain ...'

These types of questions require you to give an idea of, for example, how something works, what is involved in a process or specific features of a design. It usually involves writing one or two sentences. Often these questions allocate two marks and will require you to justify your answer with a 'because'.

Example question:

(d) Describe how the Ø 60 mm hole could be cut in the wooden back. [2]

'Complete ...'

This type of question requires you to complete, for example, a design, drawing or table.

Example question:

(e) Complete the table by describing what each of the tools or items of equipment is used for when making the wooden back. [4]

'Use sketches and notes to ...'

This is used to invite you to produce a design to solve a specific problem. It is essential that sketches are used as the main part of the answer and that they are large and clear. The written notes must support and expand on the sketches and they must be technically accurate.

These questions sometimes have a high mark allocation of four, five or six marks.

Example question:

(f) The clock will be hung on a wall. Use sketches and notes to show how this could be done. Include details of any fittings you would use. [3]

Tool or item of equipment	What is each of the tools or items of equipment used for?
Template	
Tenon saw	
Sanding machine	
Varnish	

Table 9.1

'Explain ...'

This requires a detailed account of something, including reasons, justifications, and possibly comparisons and examples. This type of question always carries at least two marks. In the example below, you would need to compare both methods of manufacture in order to justify your choice.

Example question:

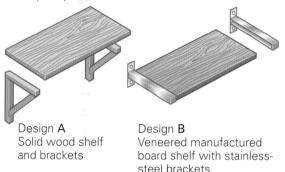

Design **A**
Solid wood shelf and brackets

Design **B**
Veneered manufactured board shelf with stainless-steel brackets

Figure 9.2

2. Figure 9.2 shows two different shelf and bracket designs. Both designs are manufactured and sold as self-assembly products.

(a) Explain which of the two designs would be more expensive to manufacture in quantity.   [2]

'Discuss ...'

When you are asked to discuss something, you must give well-reasoned points and explanations, adding examples to show the examiner what you are thinking. One-word answers are not acceptable. You need to practise these types of questions, which are the most difficult.

Example question:

(b) Discuss the impact that self-assembly has had on the design of many household products. [3]

Design question

Part of Question 4 on the examination paper is a design question and is worth 18 marks.

Example question:

3. The diagram in Figure 9.3 gives the dimensions of a spice jar. You are asked to design a *revolving* spice rack. The rack must hold six jars and rotate through 360 degrees to allow easy access to each jar.

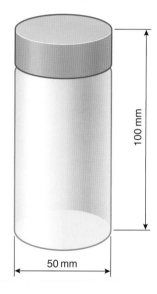

100 mm

50 mm

Figure 9.3

Specification: The design must:

• securely hold six spice jars

• allow jars to be easily removed

• rotate through 360 degrees.

Draw one idea for the rotating spice rack. Use notes to explain your idea.

Sketch your solution on the opposite page.

• Generate one idea to satisfy specification.   [8]

• Specify suitable materials.   [3]

• Specify details needed to satisfy specification.   [3]

• Quality of communication.   [4]

The design question has a large allocation of marks and is therefore a very important question on the paper. It is vital that you read the question carefully and answer each requirement. The examiner will reward each of the points, so make sure that each of these points is answered and they can be clearly identified in your answer. Name specific materials, say why they are appropriate, and provide accurate information about construction, assembly or finish.

You will always be rewarded for the 'quality of communication', so ensure your answer is well presented, clear and well annotated.

CHAPTER 10

UNIT 2: CONTROLLED ASSESSMENT TASK (CAT)

By the end of this chapter you should have developed a knowledge and understanding of how to successfully prepare for and tackle the Controlled Assessment Task (CAT) by being able to:

- respond to a design brief
- produce a design specification
- generate and communicate a range of design ideas
- develop and produce a final design proposal
- plan the making of a product
- make a product
- solve technical problems
- record the stages of making a product
- test and evaluate the product, leading to proposals for further improvement.

 This unit of the GCSE course requires you to complete a 30-hour design, make and evaluate task, known as a Controlled Assessment Task (CAT). It is worth 60 per cent of your total marks for the GCSE qualification.

The CAT is designed to enable you to fully demonstrate the designing and making skills, along with the technical knowledge, you have acquired during the first year of your GCSE course.

The completed CAT must be presented only on the 14 A3 pages using the pre-printed worksheets provided. The work must be completed strictly within the 30 hours allowed and will be marked by your teacher and moderated by the WJEC using the assessment criteria for this unit.

Important guidelines and procedures

The CAT should be an accurate reflection of **30 hours of your work**. You should make your own judgements and decisions, and take responsibility for the direction in which your CAT moves. Your teacher will advise, support and assist you by suggesting approaches, alternatives and possibilities outside the 30-hour time.

It is very important that you make the most of every minute available to you by preparing thoroughly and being familiar with the following guidelines and procedures for successfully completing the CAT.

- The design briefs are provided by the WJEC each year and you are required to select one in consultation with your teacher.

- You are strongly encouraged to research/obtain inspirational research material prior to or during the assessment period and this can be referred to during the task but this material is not to be included in the material to be assessed.

- Your teachers are required to monitor and verify that the time limit is adhered to and recorded accurately and that plagiarism does not take place.

- You do not have to take the 30 hours in one block; your teacher will probably take lessons out during the CAT to help you prepare for the next stage.

- You will not gain additional credit by exceeding the time limit.

- The CAT can be carried out in the normal classroom/workshop environment.

- You are allowed supervised access to resources that may include information gathered outside the 30 hours of controlled assessment time.

- You may collaborate/confer with others in relation to the task but all assessed material must be your work only.

- Your teacher can give you limited guidance during the task in order to clarify what is to be done and to ensure that safe working practices are adhered to.

- All graphical and written work entered for this controlled assessment must be submitted on the pre-printed pages that are available for download from the WJEC website.

- The task must not exceed the 14 A3 pages provided. You are free to use ICT and CAD where appropriate.

- It is the responsibility of your centre to ensure the reliability and authenticity of all work presented for this controlled assessment.

- Teachers and students will be required to sign a declaration that all work presented is the work of the candidate alone.

- Failure to authenticate the work may result in grades being delayed or refused.

Assessment and submission of the CAT

The project is not just about assessment and helping you to gain a qualification; it is also about you enjoying your work, demonstrating your creativity and 'learning by doing' this task.

You should structure your work to follow the assessment criteria in order to maximise your marks.

The A3 worksheets

It is recommended that you spend about ten hours completing the worksheets.

You must complete all work on the pre-printed A3 sheets and this must be confined to the 14 pages provided. You can produce your work by hand or using ICT, but you should remember that it is the content of the work that is important and no extra marks will be gained just by word processing your work, for example.

Importance of choosing the right design brief

You will have to select a design brief as a starting point for your designing and making. Your teacher will give you a maximum of three briefs in your teaching group.

Typical briefs

Listed below are some typical briefs set by the examination board. These should be used as a guide only, as the briefs set by the examination board will change from year to year. Your teacher will give you the briefs for the examination session in which you are entered.

The purpose of the CAT is to demonstrate your abilities in designing, making and evaluating. You are free to adapt and develop the briefs to suit your own interests and situations, but you must ensure:

- you meet a real design problem – you will need to think carefully about what is needed by the user group and not just about what you would like personally

- the task is challenging, to allow you to achieve the grade you are capable of, but not so difficult that you are unable to complete the work

- you display creativity and innovation

- the result is a complete high-quality product that can be evaluated

- the task is realistic and manageable within the time and resources available, including the expertise of your teachers.

Brief 1	• Designing for young children Using an individual child or group of children, design an educational toy or game that, through an imaginative choice, will be both entertaining and teach important skills.
Brief 2	• Lighting Advances in lighting technology provide great scope for imaginative and eye-catching solutions to a range of lighting problems. Design an innovative solution to an identified need.
Brief 3	• Storage Efficient storage of small items provides particular problems and requires thoughtful and innovative solutions. Identify a particular need and design a creative solution.

Table 10.1 Typical WJEC briefs

Remember:

- you need to be realistic in your choice of project and listen to the advice of your teachers

- the size of your product is important – small, carefully designed, well-made products will often outscore larger products

- cost of materials and pre-manufactured components can be a problem.

Characteristics of a successful CAT

- Good planning and organisation

- Clear focus on what your target group would like

- Creativity and refinement

- Detailed development work

- High-quality work and attention to detail

- Understanding the impact your CAT may have on the environment

- Clear and careful communication and presentation, including computer-aided design where appropriate.

Some examples of pupil practical work

Figure 10.2 Toy train

Figure 10.3 Jewellery box

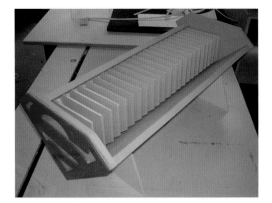

Figure 10.1 CD rack

Figure 10.4 Table light

Figure 10.5 Storage unit

The exam section by section

There is a maximum of 180 marks available for this work. These 180 marks will be divided into two sections: Section A and Section B as shown in Table 10.2.

KEY POINT

- You will need to think about how you use the time you have available. As a general rule you should allow around 20 hours to make your product.

You will need to complete and hand in the following items to your teacher when you have completed the work.

14 A3 worksheets

These will contain all of the design and evaluation work you have done. The work must be submitted on the pre-printed sheets provided.

A manufactured final product

This will be your final product made from resistant materials.

Section A	Marks
Analysis of the task	5
Writing a design specification	5
Generating ideas	10
Developing and modelling a solution: - Form/style/function [5] - Materials and components [5] - Construction [5] - Size/quantity [5] - Finish/quality [5]	25
Final solution – graphical concept	5
Final solution – technical details	5
Demonstrating creative thinking	5
Section B	
Planning the make	10
Making the product	90
Evaluation of the product	10
Suggesting improvements	10
Total:	180

Table 10.2 Section A and Section B and marks for Unit 2

▶ Section A

This section is concerned with designing the product.

Analysis of the task (5 marks)

Mark	Description of Attainment
0	No analysis presented.
1	There is a very basic analysis of where the product fits in the marketplace together with a limited evaluation of a similar product. The work presented shows little evidence of prior research and preparation. A simple brief may be evident.
2	There is a basic but appropriate analysis of where the product fits in the marketplace together with a basic evaluation of a similar product. The work presented shows limited evidence of prior research and preparation. A simple brief is evident.
3	There is a good analysis of where the product fits in the marketplace together with an evaluation of a similar product. The work presented shows some evidence of prior research and preparation. A clear brief is evident.
4	There is a very good analysis of where the product fits in the marketplace together with a detailed evaluation of a similar product. The work presented shows good evidence of prior research and preparation. A well-worded brief is evident.
5	There is a comprehensive analysis of where the product fits in the marketplace together with a very detailed evaluation of a similar product. The work presented shows clear evidence of detailed research and preparation. A clear and appropriate brief is evident.

Table 10.3 **Assessment criteria and marks for analysis of the task [5 marks]**

Analysis of the task

A good way to start this section is to use the five Ws method outlined in Chapter 1 (page 6). You will need to communicate with the user group for your product to find out exactly what they require. To do this, you can conduct a questionnaire, survey or interview and then write a conclusion about what you have found.

This page is about identifying and understanding the problem to be solved.

You should:

• clearly state which of the Controlled Assessment Task briefs you are going to tackle

• summarise the preliminary research carried out *prior* to the start of the CAT

• carry out a detailed analysis of the problem, clearly identifying the target audience for your product

• arrive at and state your own personal brief; this must clearly be based on the chosen CAT brief.

Advice and guidance:

• It is important that you carry out preliminary research to help you

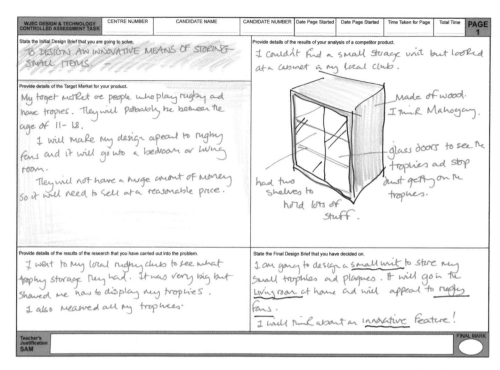

| WJEC DESIGN & TECHNOLOGY CONTROLLED ASSESSMENT TASK | CENTRE NUMBER | CANDIDATE NAME | CANDIDATE NUMBER | Date Page Started | Date Page Started | Time Taken for Page | Total Time | PAGE 1 |

State the Initial Design Brief that you are going to solve.

TO DESIGN AN INNOVATIVE MEANS OF STORING SMALL ITEMS.

Provide details of the results of your analysis of a competitor product.

I couldn't find a small storage unit but looked at a cabinet in my local club.

Made of wood.
I think Mahogany.

glass doors to see the trophies and stop dust getting on the trophies.

had two shelves to hold lots of stuff.

Provide details of the Target Market for your product.

My target market are people who play rugby and have trophies. They will probably be between the age of 11-18.

I will make my design appeal to rugby fans and it will go into a bedroom or living room.

They will not have a huge amount of money so it will need to sell at a reasonable price.

Provide details of the results of the research that you have carried out into the problem.

I went to my local rugby club to see what trophy storage they had. It was very big but showed me how to display my trophies.

I also measured all my trophies.

State the Final Design Brief that you have decided on.

I am going to design a small unit to store my small trophies and plaques. It will go in the living room at home and will appeal to rugby fans.

I will think about an innovative feature!

| Teacher's Justification SAM | | FINAL MARK |

Figure 10.6 Page 1 CAT worksheet

understand the CAT; this is not assessed or submitted.

• Preliminary work must be kept separate from the CAT and cannot be 'cut and pasted' onto the sheets.

This preliminary work does not form part of the 30-hour assessment time.

Writing a design specification
[5 marks]

This is an opportunity for you to present a detailed design specification of your intended product.

Mark	Description of Attainment
0	No specification presented.
1	A design specification comprising a list of basic attributes for the product. The specification shows little or no links with the analysis of the task. Information is poorly organised, little or no use of technical language/vocabulary. Written communication is limited in terms of organisation of material, with many errors of grammar, punctuation and spelling.
2	A basic design specification comprising a list of relevant attributes for the product. The specification shows superficial links with the analysis of the task. Information shows evidence of structure, limited use of technical language/vocabulary. Written communication is limited in terms of organisation of material with some errors of grammar, punctuation and spelling.
3	A good design specification comprising a prioritised list of attributes for the product presented under appropriate headings. The specification illustrates clear links with the analysis of the task. Information is organised, basic use of technical language/vocabulary. Written communication is adequate in terms of organisation of material, with some errors of grammar, punctuation and spelling.
4	A comprehensive design specification comprising a prioritised list of attributes for the product presented under appropriate headings. The specification demonstrates strong links with the analysis of the task. Information is well organised, good use of technical language/vocabulary. Written communication is good, presenting mainly appropriate material in a coherent manner, with few errors of grammar, punctuation and spelling.
5	An excellent design specification comprising a prioritised list of attributes for the product presented under appropriate headings. The specification is well founded in the analysis of the task. Information is well organised, presented in a highly appropriate manner, very good use of technical language/vocabulary. Written communication is good, presenting appropriate material in a coherent manner, and largely error-free.

Table 10.4 Assessment criteria and marks for writing a design specification [5 marks]

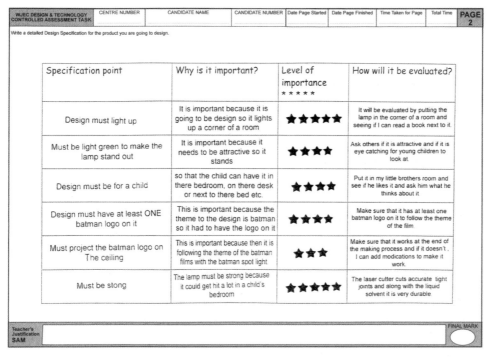

| WJEC DESIGN & TECHNOLOGY CONTROLLED ASSESSMENT TASK | CENTRE NUMBER | CANDIDATE NAME | CANDIDATE NUMBER | Date Page Started | Date Page Finished | Time Taken for Page | Total Time | PAGE 2 |

Write a detailed Design Specification for the product you are going to design.

Specification point	Why is it important?	Level of importance ★ ★ ★ ★ ★	How will it be evaluated?
Design must light up	It is important because it is going to be design so it lights up a corner of a room	★ ★ ★ ★	It will be evaluated by putting the lamp in the corner of a room and seeing if I can read a book next to it.
Must be light green to make the lamp stand out	It is important because it needs to be attractive so it stands	★ ★ ★	Ask others if it is attractive and if it is eye catching for young children to look at.
Design must be for a child	so that the child can have it in there bedroom, on there desk or next to there bed etc.	★ ★ ★	Put it in my little brothers room and see if he likes it and ask him what he thinks about it
Design must have at least ONE batman logo on it	This is important because the theme to the design is batman so it had to have the logo on it	★ ★ ★	Make sure that it has at least one batman logo on it to follow the theme of the film
Must project the batman logo on The ceiling	This is important because then it is following the theme of the batman films with the batman spot light	★ ★	Make sure that it works at the end of the making process and if it doesn't, I can add modications to make it work.
Must be stong	The lamp must be strong because it could get hit a lot in a child's bedroom	★ ★ ★ ★	The laser cutter cuts accurate tight joints and along with the liquid solvent it is very durable.

| Teacher's Justification SAM | | FINAL MARK |

Figure 10.7 Page 2 CAT worksheet

This page is about developing a detailed specification that identifies the important attributes the successful design must have.

The design specification is a list of the design requirements for the product you are designing. Detailed information about specifications can be found in Chapter 1 (page 10). The specification will give you a focus for producing design ideas and developing your work, as well as a framework for testing and evaluating your product after it has been made.

You should:

- develop a specification that is relevant and specific to the problem and brief and clearly related to the analysis

- consider a range of issues including the target user, aesthetics, function, cost, safety, etc.
- identify a hierarchy of importance
- consider quantitative and qualitative statements
- make reference to how the specification points will be measured/evaluated.

Advice and guidance:

- There is no need to produce more than *ten* specification points; you will benefit from producing fewer points, that are more detailed and specific.

Generating ideas [10 marks]

This page is about generating a wide range of initial design ideas.

Mark	Description of Attainment
0	No ideas presented. No evidence of written communication.
1–2	A small range of barely appropriate ideas that are poorly annotated. The ideas and annotation show little attention to the specification. Information is poorly organised, little or no use of technical language/vocabulary. Written communication is limited in terms of organisation of material, with many errors of grammar, punctuation and spelling.
3–4	A range of appropriate ideas that are annotated. The ideas and annotation show some attention to the specification. Information shows evidence of structure, limited use of technical language/vocabulary. Written communication in terms of organisation of material with some errors of grammar, punctuation and spelling.
5–6	A range of clear ideas that are appropriately annotated. The ideas and annotation show some attention to the specification. Information is organised, basic use of technical language/vocabulary. Written communication is adequate in terms of organisation of material, with some errors of grammar, punctuation and spelling.
7–8	A range of good initial ideas that are well annotated. The ideas and annotation show good attention to the specification. Information is well organised, good use of technical language/vocabulary. Written communication is good, presenting mainly appropriate material in a coherent manner, with few errors of grammar, punctuation and spelling.
9–10	A range of excellent initial ideas that are very well annotated. The ideas and annotation show close attention to the specification. Information is well organised, presented in a highly appropriate manner, very good use of technical language/vocabulary. Written communication is good, presenting material in a coherent manner and largely error-free.

Table 10.5 Assessment criteria and marks for generating ideas [10 marks]

You should:

- generate a *range* and *variety* of ideas on this sheet
- present your work effectively, using range of media and techniques
- annotate your work, making reference to some of the materials/production techniques you could use
- demonstrate creativity and free thinking
- ensure that your ideas reflect the specification.

Advice and guidance:

- Generally you are encouraged to use freehand sketching to present your ideas.
- You may wish to use CAD at this stage, but should be mindful of the requirements stated above and be aware of the time allocation.

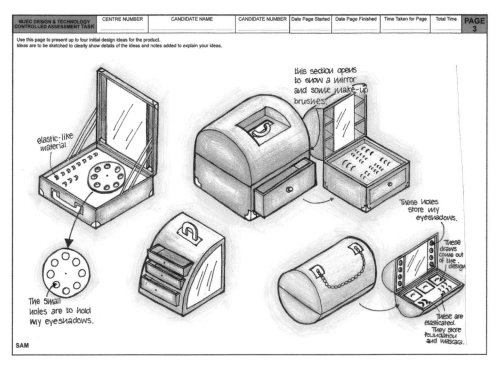

Figure 10.8 Page 3 CAT worksheet

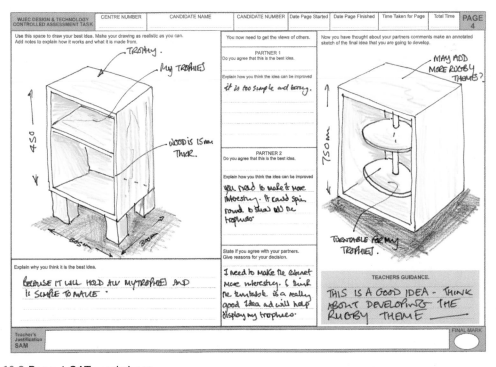

Figure 10.9 Page 4 CAT worksheet

- You should not take up excessive time 'colouring' your work.

This page is about identifying the initial idea that is going to be developed and gathering the views of the designer and others.

You should:

- draw and state clearly the initial idea to be developed
- justify your decision
- gather the views of two other people in your group
- evaluate the views of others
- identify the aspects of your design you are going to develop.

Advice and guidance:

- There is no need to develop more than one idea, although you may incorporate features of other ideas in your development.

- You may wish to summarise the views of others in your own words or get your partners to write in the space provided.

Developing and modelling a solution (25 marks)

You need to choose your best idea and develop it into its final form. This section is an opportunity for you to use appropriate ICT. Marks are awarded for evidence of development under the headings shown. You must offer options and make reasoned decisions under each heading. Evidence of these areas may be presented in integrated form across the five pages available. The 25 marks are divided into the following five sections:

Mark	Description of Attainment
0	No development of form presented.
1	Limited evidence of the form/style being developed or modelled. An alternative shape or style may be evident. There is no evidence of decision making.
2	Some evidence of the form/style being developed or modelled. Several options are presented. There is evidence of decision making but with little reasoning offered.
3	Clear evidence of the form/style being developed or modelled. Several options have been offered. There is evidence of reasoned decision making.
4	Good evidence of the form/style being developed and modelled. Several appropriate options have been offered. There is clear evidence of informed decision making.
5	A variety of forms/styles has been presented and the shape and form of the product have been developed and modelled in a progressive way. A final decision based on sound reasoning has been made.

Table 10.6 Assessment criteria and marks for form/style [5 marks]

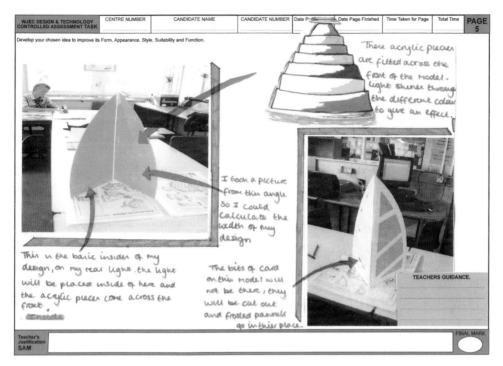

Figure 10.10 Page 5 CAT worksheet

This page is about developing the form, style and function of the chosen idea.

You should consider:

the function:

- what the design must do
- what it must store or include

the aesthetics:

- what the design looks like and how it can be improved
- colour schemes.

Advice and guidance:

- You should be encouraged to justify changes in this section.
- At the end of this section the developed solution may bear little resemblance to the initial idea or be very similar.
- Models can be made and photographs pasted onto the sheet.
- CAD may be used if considered appropriate.

Page 6: Materials/components

This page is about demonstrating a knowledge and understanding of a range of materials and components that could be used.

Mark	Description of Attainment
0	No development of materials/components presented.
1	Limited evidence of the selection of appropriate materials/components. Materials/components have been stated. There is no evidence of decision making.
2	Some evidence of the selection of appropriate materials/components. Alternatives have been offered. There is some evidence of decision making.
3	Clear evidence of the selection of appropriate materials/components. Alternatives have been offered. There is evidence of reasoned decision making.
4	Clear evidence of the selection of appropriate materials/components. Appropriate alternatives have been offered. There is clear evidence of reasoned decision making.
5	Full and clear evidence of the selection of appropriate materials/components. Appropriate alternatives have been offered. There is evidence of well-reasoned decision making.

Table 10.7 Assessment criteria and marks for selection of materials/components [5 marks]

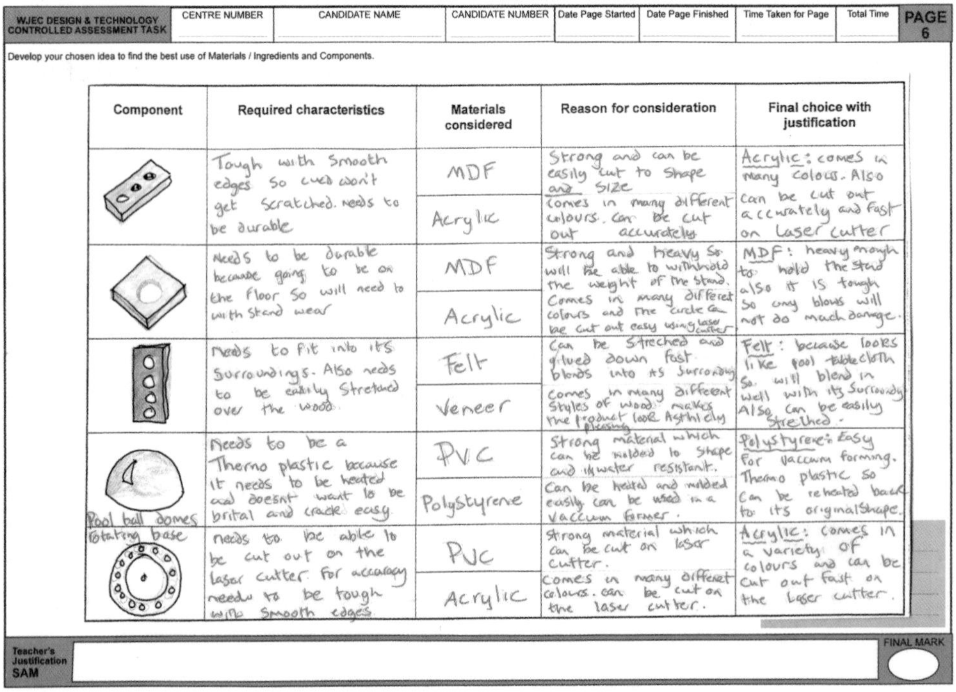

WJEC DESIGN & TECHNOLOGY CONTROLLED ASSESSMENT TASK | CENTRE NUMBER | CANDIDATE NAME | CANDIDATE NUMBER | Date Page Started | Date Page Finished | Time Taken for Page | Total Time | PAGE 6

Develop your chosen idea to find the best use of Materials / Ingredients and Components.

Component	Required characteristics	Materials considered	Reason for consideration	Final choice with justification
	Tough with Smooth edges So cues won't get Scratched. needs to be durable	MDF	Strong and can be easily cut to Shape and Size	Acrylic: comes in many colours. Also can be cut out accurately and fast on Laser cutter
		Acrylic	Comes in many different colours. Can be cut out accurately	
	Needs to be durable because going to be on the floor So will need to with stand wear	MDF	Strong and heavy So will be able to withhold the weight of the stand.	MDF: heavy enough to hold the stand also it is tough so any blows will not do much damage.
		Acrylic	Comes in many differet colours and the circle can be cut out easy using laser cutter	
	needs to fit into its Surroundings. Also needs to be easily Stretched over the wood	Felt	Can be Streched and glued down fast blends into its Surrounding	Felt: because looks like pool tablecloth So will blend in well with its Surrounding Also can be easily Streched.
		Veneer	Comes in many different Styles of wood makes the product look Asthicly pleasing	
Pool ball domes	Needs to be a Thermo plastic because it needs to be heated and doesnt want to be brital and crack easy	PVC	Strong material which can be molded to Shape and is water resistant.	Polystyrene: Easy for vaccum forming. Thermo plastic so can be reheated back to its originalShape.
		Polystyrene	Can be heated and molded easily can be used in a vaccum former.	
rotating base	needs to be able to be cut out on the laser cutter for accuracy needs to be tough with Smooth edges	PVC	Strong material which can be cut on laser cutter.	Acrylic: comes in a variety of colours and can be cut out fast on the Laser cutter.
		Acrylic	Comes in many differet colours. can be cut on the laser cutter.	

Teacher's Justification SAM | FINAL MARK

Figure 10.11 Page 6 CAT worksheet

You should suggest and consider a range of possible materials and make reasoned decisions based on a variety of criteria that may include:

- aesthetics: colour, decoration, pattern, etc.
- function: durability, weight, strength, conductivity, ease of use, etc.
- cost
- availability
- safety.

Advice and guidance:

- It is important that you relate this section directly to your product and do not simply produce a table of materials.

Page 7: Construction/making

This page is about exploring and demonstrating knowledge and understanding of a range of ways of making/constructing the idea.

Mark	Description of Attainment
0	No development of the construction/making presented.
1	Limited evidence of the construction/making being developed. A construction/making method has been offered. There is no evidence of decision making.
2	Some evidence of the construction being developed. A small variety of construction/making methods has been offered. There is some evidence of decision making.
3	Clear evidence of the construction/making being developed. A variety of construction/making methods has been offered. There is evidence of reasoned decision making.
4	Clear evidence of the construction/making being developed. A variety of appropriate construction/making methods has been considered. There is evidence of well-reasoned decision making.
5	Full and clear evidence of the construction/making being developed. A range of appropriate construction/making methods has been considered. There is evidence of well-reasoned decision making.

Table 10.8 Assessment criteria and marks for construction/making [5 marks]

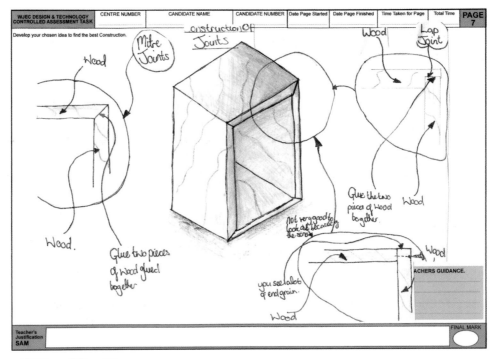

Figure 10.12 Page 7 CAT worksheet

You should:

- consider different ways of constructing the product. These may include:
  - different joints
  - permanent and temporary fixings
  - different processes
  - use of CAD/CAM
  - joining like and unlike materials
- annotate and justify decisions.

Advice and guidance:

- You may include CAD drawings of jointing systems.
- It is important that the construction methods considered are relevant and related directly to the product, reflecting the materials you will use.

Page 8: Size and quantity

This page is about developing and arriving at
the size and/or quantity of the design.

Mark	Description of Attainment
0	No development of size/quantity presented.
1	Limited evidence of sizes and/or quantities being developed. Sizes or quantities may be evident. There is no evidence of decision making.
2	Some evidence of sizes and/or quantities being developed. Alternative sizes and/or quantities will be evident. There is some evidence of decision making.
3	Clear evidence of sizes and/or quantities being developed. Alternative sizes and/or quantities will be evident. There is evidence of reasoned decision making.
4	Clear evidence of sizes and/or quantities being developed. Sizes and/or quantities have been developed in a progressive way. There is evidence of reasoned decision making.
5	Full and clear evidence of sizes and/or quantities being developed. Alternative sizes and/or quantities have been systematically evaluated. There is clear evidence of well-reasoned decision making.

Table 10.9 Assessment criteria and marks for development of size/quantity [5 marks]

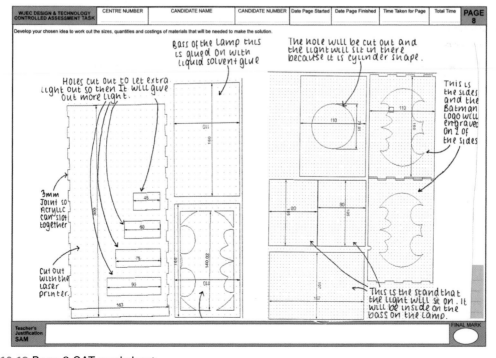

Figure 10.13 Page 8 CAT worksheet

You should consider aspects such as:

- dimensions of parts, components or products the design must hold
- the number of parts, components or products the design must hold
- where the design will go
- how it can be used efficiently
- multiple numbers of identical parts.

Advice and guidance:

- You will generally need to refer back to your preliminary research regarding dimensions of parts, components or products.
- You must justify and annotate your reasoning.
- Some reference to maximum sizes, cutting or working areas of machinery, equipment or materials may be necessary.

Page 9: Finish and quality

This page is concerned with how the design will be finished and the quality-control issues necessary to achieve a quality finish.

Mark	Description of Attainment
0	No development of finish/quality presented.
1	Limited evidence of the development of finish/quality. A suitable finish may be offered. There is no reference to quality control. There is no evidence of decision making.
2	Some evidence of the development of finish/quality. An alternative finish is offered. There is brief reference to quality control. There is evidence of decision making.
3	Some evidence of the development of finish/quality. Alternative finishes are offered. There is reference to aspects of quality control. There is evidence of decision making.
4	Clear evidence of the development of finish/quality. Alternative finishes are offered. There is reference to aspects of quality control. There is evidence of reasoned decision making.
5	Full and clear evidence of the development of finish/quality. A range of alternative finishes is offered. There is reference to a variety of quality control issues. There is evidence of well-reasoned decision making.

Table 10.10 Assessment criteria and marks for development of finish/quality [5 marks]

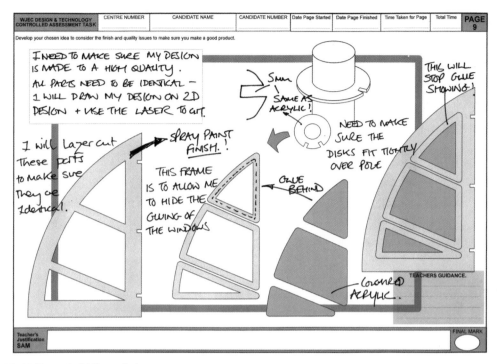

WJEC DESIGN & TECHNOLOGY CONTROLLED ASSESSMENT TASK	CENTRE NUMBER	CANDIDATE NAME	CANDIDATE NUMBER	Date Page Started	Date Page Finished	Time Taken for Page	Total Time	PAGE 9

Develop your chosen idea to consider the finish and quality issues to make sure you make a good product.

I NEED TO MAKE SURE MY DESIGN IS MADE TO A HIGH QUALITY.
AL PARTS NEED TO BE IDENTICAL –
1 WILL DRAW MY DESIGN ON 2D DESIGN + USE THE LASER TO CUT.

5mm
SAME AS ACRYLIC!

THIS WILL STOP GLUE SHOWING!

NEED TO MAKE SURE THE DISKS FIT TIGHTLY OVER POLE

I will lazer cut These parts to make sure They are 1dentical.

SPRAY PAINT FINISH.!

THIS FRAME IS TO ALLOW ME TO HIDE THE GLUING OF THE WINDOWS

GLUE BEHIND

COLOURED ACRYLIC.

TEACHERS GUIDANCE.

Teacher's Justification SAM

FINAL MARK

Figure 10.14 Page 9 CAT worksheet

You should consider:

- a range of possible finishes
- the processes/stages necessary to achieve a quality finish
- the advantages and disadvantages of each finish
- accuracy and consistency
- time allocation
- skill levels required
- ability to justify all decisions
- the relevant quality-control issues to achieve a good finish.

Advice and guidance:

- For self-finished materials such as plastic sheet you may need to focus on the edge treatment.

- It is important that this section focuses on the final product and considers all the parts of the design.
- You should be encouraged to refer to this sheet before applying the final finish.

Final solution – graphical concept

This is an opportunity for you to give full details of your final design using presentation techniques appropriate to the chosen focus area. Details of the form, dimensions, construction, components, materials and finish will be included as appropriate.

This section is an opportunity to use appropriate ICT. Marks are awarded for:

(a) a graphical presentation of the final design [5 marks]

(b) the technical details that support manufacture [5 marks].

(a) Graphical presentation [5 marks]

This is an opportunity for the candidate to present a clear and expressive graphical presentation of their final design. Any appropriate method of communication may be used.

Mark	Description of Attainment
0	No graphical presentation presented.
1	A basic illustration of the final product. It is recognisable but lacks proper form. It offers little evidence of shading or colour rendering.
2	An illustration of the final product. It is recognisable and shows reasonable form. It offers evidence of shading and/or colour rendering.
3	A clear illustration of the final product. It is recognisable and shows good form. It offers evidence of good shading and/or colour rendering.
4	A very good graphical presentation of the final product. It uses a recognised graphical technique, is accurate in its structure and shows effective shading and/or colour rendering.
5	A very high-quality graphical presentation of the final product. It uses a recognised graphical technique, is accurate in its structure and shows expressive shading and/or colour rendering.

Table 10.11 Assessment criteria and marks for graphical presentation [5 marks]

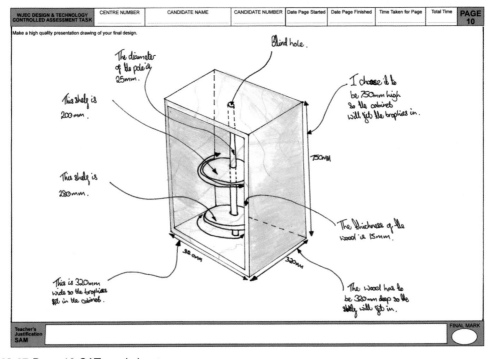

Figure 10.15 Page 10 CAT worksheet

Page 10 is about producing an accurate presentation drawing of the final design.

You should:

- use any technique you are familiar with and confident in using
- ensure an accurate representation of the final design
- use colour rendering to represent materials and finishes.

Advice and guidance:

- This is a good opportunity for using CAD but it is not compulsory.
- You can use 3D and 2D drawings as appropriate.

Final solution – technical details

This page is about providing the technical details necessary for the product to be manufactured.

(a) Technical details [5 marks]

This is an opportunity for candidates to present the final technical details of their design. These could include dimensions, materials/components, construction and finish as appropriate to each focus area.

Mark	Description of Attainment
0	No technical details presented.
1	Limited evidence of technical detail.
2	Evidence of some technical detail.
3	Evidence of many technical details.
4	Evidence of most technical details.
5	Evidence of virtually all technical details.

Table 10.12 Assessment criteria and marks for technical details [5 marks]

You should consider:

- the dimensions of each component
- how the design is constructed
- the materials used
- the finishes applied.

Advice and guidance:

You can use any format you are confident in using; this may include:

- CAD
- orthographic drawing
- exploded drawing
- step by step.

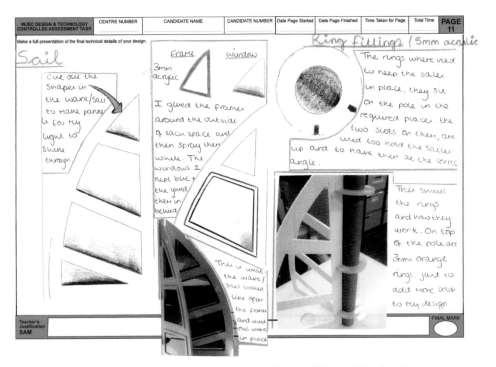

Figure 10.16 Page 11 CAT worksheet

Demonstrating creative thinking

This is an opportunity to show a measure of flair, imagination and creativity in your designing. It can be evident at any stage through the design process.

Mark	Description of Attainment
0	No creative thinking presented.
1	Evidence of limited creative thinking.
2	Evidence of some creative thinking.
3	Evidence of creative thinking in several areas.
4	Evidence of much creative thinking. Some ideas show imagination and flair. Creative thinking is evident throughout the development of the product and imaginative presentational techniques are evident.
5	A high level of creative thinking. Very imaginative ideas are evident. A highly creative development of the product is evident. Presentational techniques show much flair.

Table 10.13 Assessment criteria and marks for demonstrating creative thinking [5 marks]

Creative thinking is assessed throughout the CAT. You will be rewarded for:

- demonstrating creative thinking
- generating imaginative ideas
- demonstrating flair when presenting work.

▶ Section B

Section B is about:

- planning the manufacture of the product

- ensuring that the making is completed within the 20 hours
- ensuring you understand the processes and procedures necessary to make the product
- manufacturing a quality product
- carrying out a detailed evaluation.

Page 12: Planning the make

This page is about creating a detailed plan for manufacture.

Mark	Description of Attainment
0	No plan for making presented.
1–2	A list of manufacturing steps is evident but shows little appreciation of the work involved or the time needed.
3–4	A list of basic manufacturing steps is evident. The steps contain some detail of the processes required. There is little attempt to quantify the time needed.
5–6	A list of realistic manufacturing steps is evident. The steps contain some detail of the processes required. There is an attempt to quantify the time needed.
7–8	A list of realistic manufacturing steps is evident. The steps contain some detail of the processes required and note any constraints. There is a realistic estimate of the time needed to manufacture the outcome.
9–10	A clear, appropriate and detailed list of manufacturing steps is evident. Constraints have been recognised. There is a realistic estimate of the time needed to manufacture the outcome.

Table 10.14 Planning the make [10 marks]

You should consider:

- a logical procedure for making
- breaking the making down into a series of stages
- the time allocation for each stage

- all the processes involved
- quality-control issues.

Advice and guidance:

- Use a variety of approaches including Gantt charts and critical-path analysis.

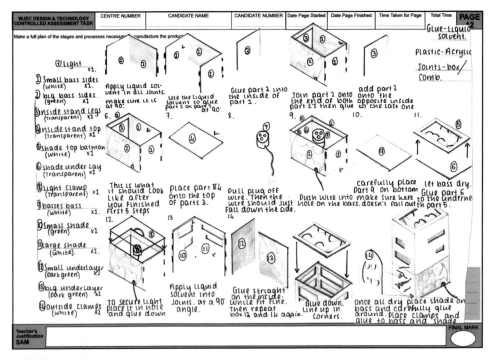

Figure 10.17 Page 12 CAT worksheet

Making the product

There are 90 marks allocated for the practical work.

Range and difficulty of practical processes	10
Quality of construction	25
Dimensional accuracy	15
Quality of finish/appearance	15
Function	10
Independent working	15

Table 10.15 Allocation of marks for the practical work

Mark	Description of Attainment
0	No practical processes evident.
1–2	One straightforward practical process is evident.
3–4	One or two more demanding practical processes are evident.
5–6	A range of fairly demanding practical processes is evident.
7–8	A range of demanding practical processes is evident.
9–10	A range of challenging practical processes is evident.

Table 10.16 Range and difficulty of practical processes [10 marks]

Mark	Description of Attainment
0	No practical processes evident.
1–5	Little acceptable accuracy is evident in the construction/making.
6–10	An adequate level of accuracy is evident in only a few aspects of the construction/making.
11–15	An adequate level of accuracy is evident in some aspects of the construction/making.
16–20	A good level of accuracy is evident in all aspects of the construction/making.
21–25	A high level of accuracy is evident in all aspects of the construction/making.

Table 10.17 Quality of construction/making [25 marks]

Mark	Description of Attainment
0	No practical processes evident.
1–3	The finished product bears little resemblance to the final design proposal.
4–6	The finished product matches some details, both visual and technical, of the final design proposal.
7–9	The finished product matches many details, both visual and technical, of the final design proposal.
10–12	The finished product matches most details, both visual and technical, of the final design proposal.
13–15	The finished product matches virtually all details, both visual and technical, of the final design proposal.

Table 10.18 Dimensional accuracy [15 marks]

Mark	Description of Attainment
0	No practical processes evident.
1–3	No elements of the product display an adequate finish.
4–6	Some elements of the product display an adequate finish.
7–9	Most elements of the product display an adequate finish.
10–12	Most elements of the product display a good finish.
13–15	Great care is taken to achieve a very high-quality finish on all elements of the product.

Table 10.19 Quality of finish/appearance [15 marks]

Mark	Description of Attainment
0	The product does not function on any level.
1–2	The product functions in a very limited or partially finished way.
3–4	The product functions to a limited extent.
5–6	The product functions fairly well.
7–8	The product functions well.
9–10	The product functions perfectly.

Table 10.20 Function [10 marks]

Mark	Description of Attainment
0	The candidate cannot work without constant support and advice.
1–2	The candidate has required considerable support and advice during the making of the product.
3–4	The candidate has required fairly frequent support and advice during the making of the product.
5–6	The candidate has required some support and advice during the making of the product.
7–8	The candidate has required only minor support and advice during the making of the product.
9–10	The candidate has worked almost entirely unaided whilst making the product.

Table 10.21 Independent working [10 marks]

Evaluation of the product

This page is about evaluating the final product.

Mark	Description of Attainment
0	No evaluation presented. No evidence of written communication.
1–2	A basic evaluation of the outcome is evident. Comments are general and do not relate back to the initial specification. Information is poorly organised, little or no use of technical language/vocabulary. Written communication is limited in terms of organisation of material, with many errors of grammar, punctuation and spelling.
3–4	An evaluation of the outcome is evident. Comments offer some detail and relate in part back to the initial specification. Information shows evidence of structure, limited use of technical language/vocabulary. Written communication is limited in terms of organisation of material, with some errors of grammar, punctuation and spelling.
5–6	A critical evaluation of the outcome is evident. Comments offer some detail and relate in part back to the initial specification. Information is organised, with basic use of technical language/vocabulary. Written communication is adequate in terms of organisation of material, with some errors of grammar, punctuation and spelling.
7–8	A critical evaluation of the outcome is evident. The comments are perceptive and detailed and relate back to the initial specification. Information is well organised, with good use of technical language/vocabulary. Written communication is good, presenting mainly appropriate material in a coherent manner, with few errors of grammar, punctuation and spelling.
9–10	A critical evaluation of the outcome is evident. The comments are perceptive and detailed and relate in full back to the initial specification. Information is well organised, presented in a highly appropriate manner, very good use of technical language/vocabulary.

Table 10.22 Evaluation of the product [10 marks]

The specification:

- Evaluate how the product meets each specification point.
- Be critical but constructive.
- Provide evidence where appropriate to back up conclusions.

Views of others:

- Ask the opinion of the two persons named on Page 4 CAT worksheet.
- Does the designer agree/disagree?
- Provide reasoned responses.

General conclusions:

- How the design meets the needs of the target audience.
- Time management.
- Quality-control issues.
- General difficulties/successes.

Advice and guidance:

- You are expected to produce a piece of continuous writing; you may use tables, bullet points or subheadings but need to write in full sentences.

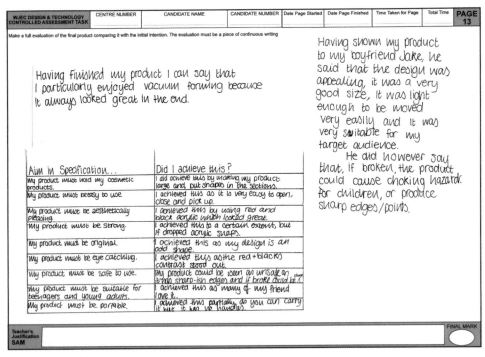

Figure 10.18 Page 13 CAT worksheet

Mark	Description of Attainment
0	No improvements presented. No evidence of written communication.
1–2	An improvement to the design and/or manufacturing process has been suggested. Written communication is limited in terms of organisation of material, with many errors of grammar, punctuation and spelling.
3–4	Several suggestions for improvements to the design together with a suggestion of how quality of manufacture could be improved. Written communication is limited in terms of organisation of material, with some errors of grammar, punctuation and spelling.
5–6	Several relevant suggestions for improvements to the design together with suggestions of how quality of manufacture could be improved. Quality of written communication is basic, some errors of grammar, punctuation and spelling.
7–8	Well-founded suggestions for improvements to the design together with suggestions of how quality of manufacture could be improved. Information is well organised, with good use of technical language/vocabulary. Written communication is good, presenting mainly appropriate material in a coherent manner, few errors of grammar, punctuation and spelling.
9–10	Well-founded suggestions for improvements to the design together with detailed suggestions of how quality of manufacture could be improved. Information is well organised, with very good use of technical language/vocabulary. Quality of written communication is good, presenting appropriate material in a coherent manner, and largely error-free.

Table 10.23 Evaluation of suggesting improvements [10 marks]

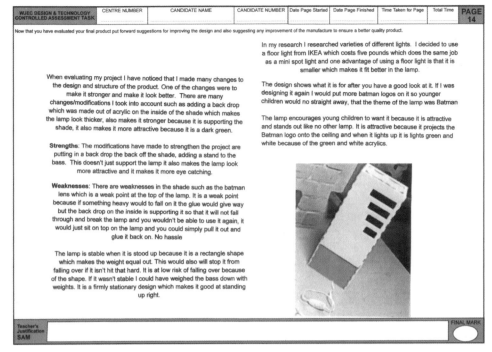

| WJEC DESIGN & TECHNOLOGY CONTROLLED ASSESSMENT TASK | CENTRE NUMBER | CANDIDATE NAME | CANDIDATE NUMBER | Date Page Started | Date Page Finished | Time Taken for Page | Total Time | PAGE 14 |

Now that you have evaluated your final product put forward suggestions for improving the design and also suggesting any improvement of the manufacture to ensure a better quality product.

When evaluating my project I have noticed that I made many changes to the design and structure of the product. One of the changes were to make it stronger and make it look better. There are many changes/modifications I took into account such as adding a back drop which was made out of acrylic on the inside of the shade which makes the lamp look thicker, also makes it stronger because it is supporting the shade, it also makes it more attractive because it is a dark green.

Strengths: The modifications have made to strengthen the project are putting in a back drop the back off the shade, adding a stand to the bass. This doesn't just support the lamp it also makes the lamp look more attractive and it makes it more eye catching.

Weaknesses: There are weaknesses in the shade such as the batman lens which is a weak point at the top of the lamp. It is a weak point because if something heavy would to fall on it the glue would give way but the back drop on the inside is supporting it so that it will not fall through and break the lamp and you wouldn't be able to use it again, it would just sit on top on the lamp and you could simply pull it out and glue it back on. No hassle

The lamp is stable when it is stood up because it is a rectangle shape which makes the weight equal out. This would also will stop it from falling over if it isn't hit that hard. It is at low risk of falling over because of the shape. If it wasn't stable I could have weighed the bass down with weights. It is a firmly stationary design which makes it good at standing up right.

In my research I researched varieties of different lights. I decided to use a floor light from IKEA which costs five pounds which does the same job as a mini spot light and one advantage of using a floor light is that it is smaller which makes it fit better in the lamp.

The design shows what it is for after you have a good look at it. If I was designing it again I would put more batman logos on it so younger children would no straight away, that the theme of the lamp was Batman

The lamp encourages young children to want it because it is attractive and stands out like no other lamp. It is attractive because it projects the Batman logo onto the ceiling and when it lights up it is lights green and white because of the green and white acrylics.

| Teacher's Justification SAM | | FINAL MARK |

Figure 10.19 Page 14 CAT worksheet

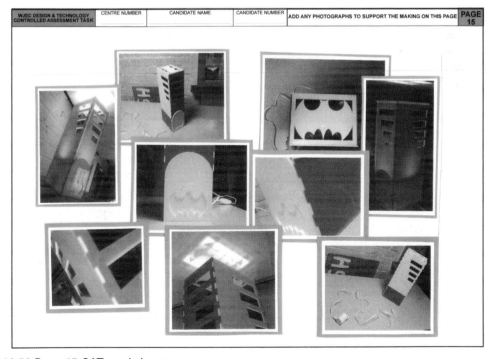

| WJEC DESIGN & TECHNOLOGY CONTROLLED ASSESSMENT TASK | CENTRE NUMBER | CANDIDATE NAME | CANDIDATE NUMBER | ADD ANY PHOTOGRAPHS TO SUPPORT THE MAKING ON THIS PAGE | PAGE 15 |

Figure 10.20 Page 15 CAT worksheet

You should:

- reflect the points identified on Page 13 CAT worksheet
- use a series of annotated sketches.

Improvements can be related to a variety of issues including:

- aesthetics
- function
- quality of manufacture
- processes used
- time allocation
- durability
- safety
- appropriateness of materials.

INDEX